THE 1943
SATURDAY
BOOK

THE CONTENTS

The first impression of this book, published in October, 1942, consists of ten thousand copies, made and printed at the Mayflower Press (of Plymouth), at St. Albans, by William Brendon & Son Ltd., and produced in complete conformity with the authorised economy standards. MSS., correspondence, etc., should be sent to the Editor, 47, Princes Gate, London, S.W.7.

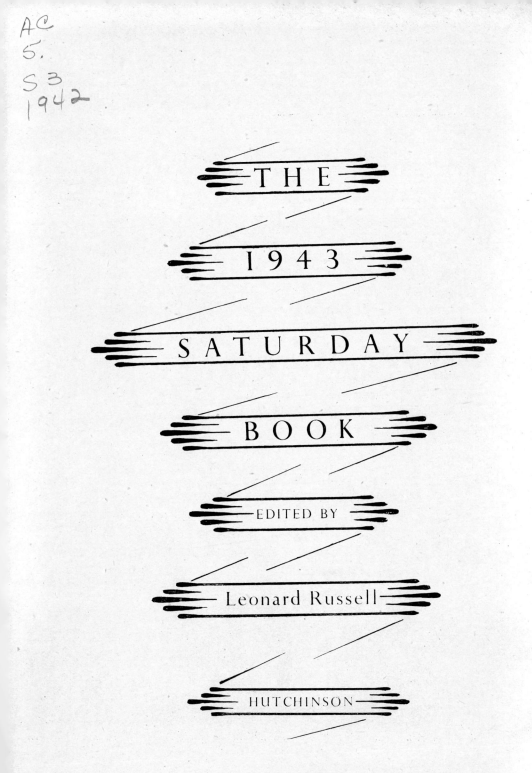

THE

1943

SATURDAY

BOOK

EDITED BY

Leonard Russell

HUTCHINSON

THE SATURDAY BOOK Office,
47 Princes Gate, London, S.W.7.

The first volume of THE SATURDAY BOOK appeared in the autumn of 1941, and since then has been read to an extent pleasing to all concerned with its production. It was not, apparently, a mistake to believe that there was room for an annual illustrated miscellany of new essays, stories, portraits, critical studies, and country notes. This second volume may be allowed to speak, however inaudibly, for itself. Constant readers will doubtless observe that actualities play a larger part here, and that the book as a whole is composed in a more contemporary key.

Pictures form an essential feature of THE SATURDAY BOOK, and the first part introduces the camera-work of DOUGLAS GLASS. Other photographers contribute to this section, and thanks are tendered to them. Parts two and three, like the first part, are about the war. They contain contributions from two well-known foreign correspondents—ALEXANDER WERTH (p. 41), author of The Last Days of Paris and Moscow 41, and WILLIAM L. SHIRER (p. 92), author of the renowned Berlin Diary. Here also is an important study of Roosevelt by Professor D. W. BROGAN (p. 70), who holds the chair of Political Science at Cambridge University ; and there are contributions by GREGOR ZIEMER (p. 88), who founded a school for the children of the American colony in Berlin and wrote Education for Death, and Squadron Leader J. A. F. MACLACHLAN, D.S.O., D.F.C. and bar (p. 56).

After warlike matters come the civilising influences of painting, music, and the drama. Thus in part four a quartet of great

D. W. BROGAN   AGNES MILLER PARKER   ALEXANDER WERTH

HAROLD HOBSON   DOUGLAS GLASS   SQ. LDR. MACLACHLAN
Painting by Eric Kennington

contemporary figures in these arts are discussed and critically considered, while the sixth part adds some marginal notes to literature, social history, and sport. The authors include THOMAS RUSSELL (p. 125), of the London Philharmonic Orchestra, and author of *Philharmonic*, ERIC NEWTON (p. 136), and PETER QUENNELL (p. 217).

Fiction formed a satisfactory feature of the first volume. Here again, in part five, the team is a strong one. JOHN STEINBECK (p. 189) is welcomed to these pages. There is a memorable short novel by H. E. BATES (p. 241). DILYS POWELL contributes 'In the Train' (p. 199). FLYING OFFICER X (p. 204) has made a literary reputation in little more than a year, and the story which he regards as his best appears here.

The final part, about animals, moves from the beautiful, through the charming, to the absurd. Again this year AGNES MILLER PARKER contributes a series of wood engravings (p. 241) ; while WILL CUPPY (p. 264) deals drastically with some of the larger creatures. Generally speaking, this book prints new matter only, but Mr. Cuppy's contribution is an exception ; it is resurrected from his *How to Tell Your Friends from the Apes* (Methuen).

Shortage of space made it impossible to include in this issue a brilliant and detailed chronicle of the first three years of the war by HAROLD HOBSON. Fortunately, however, it is not to be lost to readers, for arrangements have been made to publish it in amplified form as a S A T U R D A Y B O O K special volume.

Finally, the Editor wishes to thank Max Freedman for his indefatigable assistance and encouragement.

Part 1

WAR PICTURES

The camera has recorded many impressive moments of action in this war : the bombs, like ninepins, falling towards German soil, the desert tanks moving up to battle past the marble columns of Imperial Rome, the plane blown to powder in the bright air. These were notable, but the little picture book of the war which follows does not concern itself to any marked extent with the war of machines. It is best described, perhaps, as a social record —the war of the common people, the war in the streets, the village, the home. The scene is not always Britain. There are heartrending reminders, deliberately introduced, of the sufferings of the women of Russia, China, Greece, and other of our Allies : the contrasts between their exposure to the enemy and our relative security will not pass unnoticed. A chronicle of the war has been added to provide the large impersonal background to the personal episode.

THE LAST NIGHT of PEACE

DOUGLAS GLASS

THE FIRST DAY of WAR

At 11.30 a.m. a French military plane crossed the south coast making for Croydon. Its type was not recognised and the siren (right) sounded for the first time.

THE STEPS

DOUGLAS GLASS

BRIXHAM

LEFT BEHIND

DOUGLAS GLASS

EVACUATED

CECIL BEATON

IN POLAND MEANWHILE the annihilation of a people. Civilians are led to execution, hands tied behind backs ; and men soon to be executed dig graves for their murdered comrades.

Hyde Park Debating Point

PRINCE MONOLULU : 'They told us Hitler had missed the bus. Yes, but he did something smarter than catch a bus. He took a plane. To Norway. Where's that phoney war now ?'

BILL BRANDT

WAR CHRONICLE

SEPTEMBER, 1939

1 At 5.30 a.m. Germany invades Poland ; sixty towns and villages bombed.

3 11 a.m., Britain at war with Germany. 11.30 a.m., first air-raid warning. War Cabinet of nine ; Churchill, First Lord. Hitler undertakes, in message to Roosevelt, not to bomb civilians. SS. *Athenia* torpedoed.

4 29 R.A.F. bombers attack warships in the Schillig Roads and at Brunsbuttel. First British leaflet raid.

5 French troops move forward on Western Front.

11 B.E.F. now in France.

16 Warsaw given 12 hours to surrender.

17 Russian troops enter eastern Poland.

18 Loss of aircraft-carrier *Courageous* ; junction of German-Soviet troops near Brest Litovsk.

19 Hitler announces 'secret weapon.'

23 Petrol rationing begins.

27 Warsaw surrenders after 27 days' siege.

29 German-Soviet partition of Poland.

OCTOBER

6 Hitler's peace plan.

12 Chamberlain rejects Hitler's proposals.

13 Battleship *Royal Oak* sunk by U-boat.

16 First German air raid : warships attacked in Firth of Forth.

19 Anglo-French Treaty with Turkey.

NOVEMBER

1 Finnish delegates, in Moscow, discuss Russian proposals.

2 U.S. arms embargo lifted, making possible 'cash-and-carry.'

7 Peace appeal by King of Belgians and Queen of Holland.

8 Bomb explosion, Munich beerhall.

13 First enemy bombs on British soil—Shetlands.

18 First sea-mines (magnetic mines) dropped by enemy aircraft.

21 Savings certificates and defence bonds issued.

30 Russia invades Finland, bombs Helsinki.

DECEMBER

13 Battle of the River Plate.

17 *Graf Spee* scuttles herself.

JANUARY, 1940

5 Hore-Belisha, War Minister, resigns.

8 Rationing of butter, sugar, bacon, begins.

27 Announced winter has been severest for 46 years ; Thames frozen at Kingston.

FEBRUARY

15 Mannerheim Line entered.

16 British seamen rescued from prison-ship *Altmark*.

MARCH

11 Chamberlain says Allies are prepared, in response to appeal for further aid, ' to proceed immediately and jointly to the help of Finland.'

12 Russo-Finnish peace treaty.

16 Enemy air attack on shore bases, Orkneys.

18 Hitler and Mussolini meet, Brenner Pass.

19 R.A.F. attack Sylt (first R.A.F. bombs deliberately dropped on land target— reprisal for Orkneys raid).

21 Reynaud, Premier ; Daladier, Defence Minister.

28 Britain and France agree not to negotiate separate peace or armistice.

(continued on page 16)

HOLLAND: *Father and Daughter*

BELGIUM: *The Refugees*

HIDING *from the* HERRENVOLK

DUNKIRK

ARE THEY COMING?

JUNE 10, 1940

Yellow
Cæsar

DOUGLAS GLASS

WAR CHRONICLE

APRIL, 1940

3 Lord Woolton Food Minister.
4 Chamberlain says Hitler missed the bus.
8 Allied statements on mine-laying in Norwegian waters.
9 Germany invades Denmark and Norway.
10 First battle of Narvik.
13 Second battle of Narvik.
16 Allied forces land in Norway.

MAY

1–3 Allied troops south of Trondheim withdraw.
7–8 Debate in House on Norway.
10 Germany invades Holland, Belgium and Luxemburg. British and French troops enter Belgium. Chamberlain resigns, Churchill Premier.
11 Germans cross Albert Canal.
14 Germans reach Meuse from Liége to Namur. Dutch forces cease resistance. Home Guard (Local Defence Volunteers) founded.
15 Germans cross Meuse.
16 Churchill consults with Reynaud in Paris.
17 B.E.F. withdrawn west of Brussels.
18 Pétain, Vice-Premier.
19 Weygand, C.-in-C.
21 Germans thrust on to Arras, Amiens, Abbeville ; British counter-attack.
22 Emergency Bill giving Government control over persons and property.
23 Fighting in Boulogne. Mosley and Ramsay arrested.

27 Fall of Calais.
28 Belgian Army capitulates. Narvik captured.
29 British and French Armies fighting their way to 'fortified camp at Dunkirk.'
30 Large Dunkirk evacuations.

JUNE

4 In the House, Churchill, in a great speech, says we have suffered 'a colossal military disaster.' But by 'a miracle of deliverance' 335,000 allied troops saved from Dunkirk. 'We shall go on,' he says, 'to the end. . . . We shall fight on the beaches. We shall fight on the landing-grounds. . . . We shall never surrender.'
5 The Battle of France opens along Somme and eastward. Cripps, Ambassador to Russia.
7 First V.C. awarded posthumously to Capt. Warburton-Lee.
9 Norwegians cease hostilities.
10 Italy declares war. Announced Allied forces withdrawn from Narvik.
11 French retire across Marne.
14 Germans enter Paris.
16 Britain's offer of act of union with France rejected. Pétain succeeds Reynaud.
17 Pétain asks for armistice.
18 Hitler and Mussolini meet at Munich.
21 Hitler gives French delegates Armistice terms in Foch's railway coach.
24 French Armistice with Italy signed.
25 Hostilities in France end.
28 De Gaulle recognised as Free French leader.

(continued on page 20)

BELGIUM
in
BRITAIN

DOUGLAS GLASS

TIN HATS for DAYLIGHT RAIDS

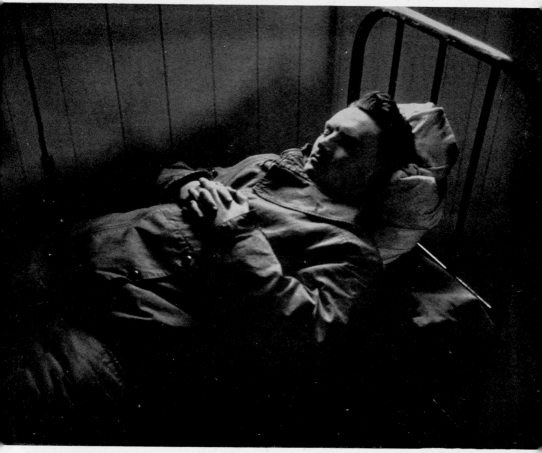

HUMPHREY SPENDER

WAR CHRONICLE

JULY, 1940

3 Naval action against French fleet at Oran.
9 Tea rationing begins ; restaurant meals to be restricted.
17 Britain agrees close Burma Road for three months.
19 Hitler makes a 'last appeal to common sense.'

AUGUST

4 Italians invade Somaliland.
8 Battle of Britain begins : 60 German planes shot down in Channel.
11 British ports and shipping attacked : 60 down.
13 78 down.
14 31 down.
15 Generally believed Hitler had publicly declared he would be in London by this day—182 down.
16 75 down. Bombs on S.W. London.
18 144 down.
20 Churchill announces lease of bases to U.S. Of R.A.F. victories over Luftwaffe he says, 'Never in the field of human conflict was so much owed by so many to so few.'
24 First bombs fall in Central London.
25 39 down. First British bombs on Berlin.
26–27 First all-night raid on London.
30 62 down.
31 88 down.

(continued on page 29)

SHELTER IN THE TOMB

To the East End the dusk to dawn raids brought appalling shelter problems. Crypts, warehouses, cellars, became in effect lodging-houses, but lodging-houses devoid of the most elementary amenities. This picture and the two following were taken in September, 1940.

THE SIKH and HIS FAMILY

BILL BRANDT

WHITECHAPEL

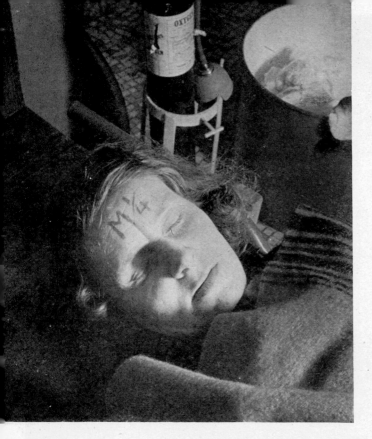

CASUALTY

One - quarter grain of morphia has been given

WHEN LONDON WAS UNDER FIRE in 1940, Britain's one
ally in arms, Greece, was under fire too. This old Greek lady sits
among the ruins of her home, a bundle of salvaged odds and ends
on her lap.

CONSTANCE WHITNEY, DIED 1628

When the first bombs fell on Central London (August 24, 1940), St. Giles's Church, Cripplegate, was hit. The memorial there to 17-year-old Constance Whitney used to show her sitting up in her coffin with hands raised, presumably flying straight to heaven. But now she is armless and coffinless. The bandage keeps the cracked head together.

DOUGLAS GLASS

BOW CHURCH
Wren's St. Mary-le-Bow, Cheapside

BOW BELLS

The steeple and Early Norman crypt of St. Mary-le-Bow survived the bombs, but the Bells nearly all came down. Their fragments are now stored in the crypt. Bow Bells of Whittington's day were lost in the fire of 1666.

WAR CHRONICLE

SEPTEMBER, 1940

3 Britain gets 50 over-age destroyers from U.S. in exchange for bases.

6 Carol of Rumania abdicates in favour of Prince Michael.

7-8 Blitz opens with mass raid on London, docks, etc. ; 103 down.

15 185 down.

16 Hitler's invasion day (according to Air Ministry News Service).

23 De Gaulle reaches Dakar, attempt to land abandoned. George Cross and Medal instituted.

27 Pact between Germany, Italy, Japan. 133 down.

OCTOBER

4 Hitler and Mussolini meet at Brenner. Portal, Chief of Air Staff.

21 Purchase Tax operative.

28 Italian invasion of Greece.

NOVEMBER

5 Roosevelt re-elected.

9 Death of Neville Chamberlain.

11 Italian fleet attacked Taranto. Italian planes raid Britain—13 down.

14-15 Coventry severely bombed.

20 Hungary joins Axis.

21 Greeks capture Koritza.

DECEMBER

6 Greeks occupy Santi Quaranta.

8 Greeks occupy Argyrokastro and Delvino.

9 Wavell begins offensive against Italians.

17 Roosevelt suggests leasing of arms.

29 Fireblitz on City of London.

JANUARY, 1941

22 Australians enter Tobruk.

FEBRUARY

6 Benghazi captured.

8 Lease-Lend Bill passed.

(continued on page 40)

WOMEN
of
RUSSIA

GREATER ASIA CO-PROSPERITY SPHERE

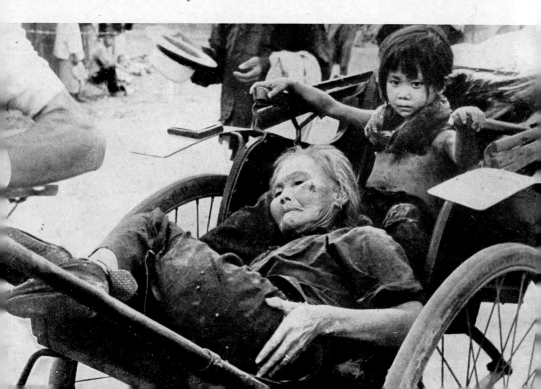

DOUGLAS GLASS

BAD NEWS FROM ASIA travels fast to
Kingsway. The seller is 75-year-old Pat McCann,
who shares a pitch outside Holborn Tube station.

DRINK
SHORTAGE

GUINNESS ... YES
BASS ... YES
WORTHINGTON ... NO
LIGHT ALE ... NO
BROWN ALE ... YES
LONDON STOUT ... NO

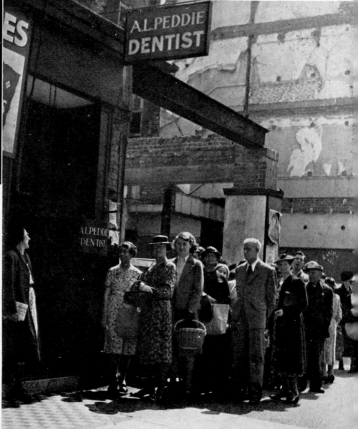

AL PEDDIE
DENTIST

DENTIST
SHORTAGE?

No—they are waiting to buy food for dogs and cats at the nearby shop.

LABOUR SHORTAGE

Margot Fonteyn, the ballerina, sews her own costumes for the *Hamlet* ballet, helped by her mother, at the Soho studio of Matilda Etches (at telephone).

DOUGLAS GLASS

SHORTAGE of PRACTICALLY EVERYTHING

DOUGLAS GLAS

DOUGLAS GLASS

BROOMS and SHOVELS

Before the war Agnes Sullivan was a waitress and Mary Hayes an office cleaner. They work now as 'dusties' in the Mountpleasant neighbourhood.

WHEN?

DOUGLAS GLASS

WAR CHRONICLE

MARCH
1 Bulgaria joins Axis.
25 Yugoslavia signs Tripartite Pact.
27 Yugoslavia revolts.
28 Battle of Cape Matapan.

APRIL
6 Germany invades Yugoslavia, Greece.
12 Enemy by-pass Tobruk, take Bardia. British and Greeks fall back.
22 Capitulation of Greek Army in Epirus.
27 Germans enter Athens.

MAY
10 Hess lands near Glasgow. London very heavily raided—33 down.
20 Germans invade Crete by air.
24 *Hood* sunk by *Bismarck*.
27 *Bismarck* sunk.
31 Iraqi rebels sign armistice.

JUNE
1 British withdrawal from Crete announced.
8 British and Free French invade Syria.
22 Germany invades Russia.

JULY
3 Stalin orders 'scorched earth.'
11 Fighting ends in Syria.
16 Germans claim Smolensk.

AUGUST
14 Churchill and Roosevelt issue Atlantic Charter after conference at sea.
25 British and Russians enter Iran.

SEPTEMBER
19 Germans enter Kiev.

OCTOBER
2 Hitler to his troops facing Moscow : 'To-day is the beginning of the last great decisive battle of this year.'
16 Odessa evacuated.
24 Germans claim Kharkov.

NOVEMBER
13 Neutrality Act amended.
14 *Ark Royal* sunk.
18 British offensive in Libya opens.
22 Germans enter Rostov.
30 Germans driven from Rostov.

DECEMBER
7 Japanese air attack on U.S. bases in Hawaii including Pearl Harbour.
8 U.S. and Britain declare war on Japan.
10 *Prince of Wales* and *Repulse* sunk. Russians take offensive.
11 Germany and Italy declare war on U.S.
19 Hitler makes himself C.-in-C. British evacuate Penang.
22 Japanese make big attack on Philippines.
24 British recapture Benghazi.
25 Surrender of Hong Kong.

JANUARY, 1942
2 Japanese in Manila.
9 Russians re-enter province of Smolensk.
22 Japanese land at Rabaul.
25 Japanese land at Lae.
29 Rommel retakes Benghazi

FEBRUARY
12 *Scharnhorst*, *Gneisenau* and *Prinz Eugen* escape.
15 Surrender of Singapore.
27 Battle of Java Sea.

MARCH
8 Java conquered. Japanese also take Rangoon.
10 U.S. Naval Air Arm routs Japanese fleet.
17 MacArthur, C.-in-C., Australia.
18 Lord Louis Mountbatten, Chief of Combined Operations.
28 Combined raid on St. Nazaire.

APRIL
5 Japanese air attack on Colombo.
9 *Dorsetshire*, *Cornwall*, *Hermes* sunk. U.S. forces on Bataan Peninsula surrender.
11 Indian Congress rejects British proposals.
18 Tokyo bombed by U.S. army planes.

MAY
2 Fall of Mandalay.
4–7 Battle of Coral Sea.
5 British landing, Madagascar.
13 Russian offensive in Kharkov sector.
19 German counter-offensive 80 miles south-east of Kharkov.
26 Rommel begins Libyan offensive.
28 Mexico at war with Axis.
30 1,130 R.A.F. bombers raid Cologne (44 lost).

JUNE
1 1,036 R.A.F. bombers raid Essen (35 lost).
3 Government to control coal mines.
4–7 Midway Island battle.
10 Czech village of Lidice wiped out for death of Heydrich.
11 Eden says that full understanding was reached with Molotov ' with regard to urgent task of creating a second front in Europe in 1942.'
17 British withdraw to Egyptian frontier.
21 Rommel captures Tobruk.
25 Over 1,000 bombers raid Bremen (52 lost).

JULY
1 Germans in Sevastopol. Basic petrol ration in U.K. ceases.
24 Germans claim Rostov.

AUGUST
7 Allied landing on Solomons.
9 Gandhi arrested.
11 Germans reach foothills of Caucasus.
12 Churchill in Moscow.
19 Allied raid on Dieppe.
25 The Duke of Kent killed.
26 Russian successes on central front. Battle for Stalingrad continues.

PHOTOGRAPHS in this section were also supplied by the following: Keystone, pp. 7, 12 (top), 25 (top), 30. Planet News, 24 (bottom), 25 (bottom), 31. Graphic Photo Union, 14. Topical Press, 15 (bottom). Daily Mail, 29. Polish Ministry of Information, 10. Photographs on 12 (bottom), 13, 24 (top), and the inset of a siren on 7 are Crown copyright. The inset of a newspaper seller on 14 is by Bill Brandt.

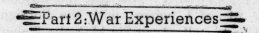

THE BURNING OF THE TEMPLE

ALEXANDER WERTH

[AUTHOR'S NOTE : *Blitz diaries tend to be monotonous ; and if I venture to publish in* THE SATURDAY BOOK *some entries from my London diary, it is only because they relate to the destruction of a cherished part of old London. I am not sure that there were any diarists among the other people who spent the whole night of the tenth of May, 1941, in or around the Temple. I apologise for some of the usual blitz clichés ; the blitz vocabulary is even poorer than the vocabulary of love.* A.W. April, 1942.]

At last I can settle down to write the story of these last two days. What a night that was ! At the moment I am looking out of my ground-floor room in Paper Buildings on to King's Bench Walk, with its green pieces of paper in the windows in place of glass ; it looks a mess, but no different from what it was a week ago. And the trees are in bud, and the grass is green in the sun, and the tulips are coming out. But you only have to go outside, and look round the corner, and the ugly results of Saturday's raid hit you in the eye. The Inner Temple Library, whose tower was wrecked early on in the blitz by an h.e., and which got its first packet of incendiaries on the night of the fireblitz last December, has now been completely burned out ; so has everything that still remained of Crown Office Row, including the house where Lamb was born, and, farther along, Lamb Building, and the Wren Cloisters, and the whole south side of Pump Court, and—worst of all—the Temple Church. The Temple Church had stood up so well to all these bombings that I had almost developed a superstitious feeling that the place was charmed ; but no, it got it this time, and most of the knights' statues lying on their tombs with their legs crossed seem to have been smashed by the collapse of the burning roof. Outside Inner Temple Library, Crown Office Row is roped off, and a notice says, 'Danger, Unexploded Bomb' . . . How did it all start ?

MONDAY
MAY 12
1941

D

YES, THAT SATURDAY was just like any other Saturday. I went to the M. of I. where, with the Foreign Office News Department, I had a talk about Sir Malcolm Robertson's report, about to be completed, on the reorganisation of the diplomatic and consular services. There had been some attacks on these services in the *Times* correspondence columns, and the F.O. were getting agitated. The situation in Iraq was said to be much more satisfactory, but there was no definite news about Syria. Freddy Kuh and Andy Rothstein were there as usual, and Kuh was all worked up about the new Oil Agreement between Japan and the Dutch East Indies, and thought Japan was preparing a southward drive as soon as she had succeeded in more or less liquidating the war in China. Andy still complained of the British Government's unfriendliness to Russia ; why hadn't we recognised the incorporation of the Baltic States in the Soviet Union ? And he was very indignant about some Estonian ships which we had not handed over to the Russians. . . .

The routine continued. Dinner at the Wellington with a bunch of people—Marion Wells, and Christie, the barrister, and Clayton of the *Mail* were there. Later we went to Christie's chambers in Lincoln's Inn. It was a lovely evening as we walked up Chancery Lane, with a moon nearly at the full. We sat about in Lincoln's Inn, drinking Christie's port and talking. At 11.30 we left.

While we walked down Chancery Lane the warning went. It was still fairly light, but almost immediately there was a zooming of planes overhead—swarms of them, though it was not light enough to see anything. At the corner of Fleet Street one of the brutes seemed to dive, and drove us into a doorway. I was glad to have my tin hat with me. However, nothing happened at first.

I was not on fire-duty that night, but I went across the road to the office to see what was going on. I told Marion she couldn't go home now, and thought she had better come to the office— one never knew. In the twilight of the first floor carpenters and painters were still working, scrapping the old partition between the subs' room and the wire room. Then I went up to the roof to see what was happening. It was George's night off, which was a pity, because there is nobody I like better to have around on a big blitz night than George with his cheery Cockney ways.

Sometimes he gets a bit nervous about 'the missus' and 'the kiddies' down at Balham, but never about anything happening to him. I found old Amos, the paid firewatcher, upstairs, and old Gibbins, the housekeeper, both with their tin hats, and with stirrup pumps and the rest, ready for action. There were firewatchers on all the big houses, ringing bells and blowing whistles, but little evidence of firewatching on the small houses below us. It was not very dark yet, and the outline of St Paul's was clearly visible. At a number of points the fires had already started, though nothing very close.

I like old Amos and old Gibbins, both over sixty and full of guts. Gibbins has a continuous broad grin on his red face whenever he sees me. He has the baggiest clothes I have ever seen, and never seems to wear a collar—only a rusty old collar stud. He has always something to grumble about, but his grumbling is so vague and inarticulate that I don't think he has ever received any satisfaction from anybody. He is a kindly old bloke, but there is one fellow he sees in the pub whom he particularly dislikes ; he refers to him as 'that one,' and once, after a few drinks, he said, 'That one, nobody loves 'im and 'e don't love nobody ; 'e don't even love 'isself.' It's the longest sentence I have ever heard him utter. He has two little rooms at the top of the building with ramshackle bits of Victorian furniture. Since the raids started he has had a rough time ; with plenty to grumble about. Sometimes because there were no firewatchers, at other times because there were too many, and they got in his way.

Old Amos is a different type. He is a gentle old soul, small and round, with a soft voice and gentle manners. He was comfortably off before the war, but his business was burned out in the first days of the blitz, his wife is dead, and one of his sons is in the Army and the other in the Navy, and 'professional' firewatching every night provides him with a living and with a chance 'to do something for the country,' as he says. Old Amos dislikes all coarseness, and one morning he told off a doddery old postman who had been sleeping on a bunk in the firewatchers' room—he was there as an 'extra' firewatcher—for 'belching and breaking wind in his sleep,' as he put it.

I stayed on the roof for a while. The sky was swarming with planes. Clang, clang, clang. The fire engines raced down Fleet Street ringing their bells. A bomb came down with a big crash some distance away. With Christie's port inside me I was feeling quite cheerful, and, going downstairs, suggested to Marion a little walk round the neighbourhood. I don't think she was enthusiastic, but she agreed. A cop was standing outside in Fleet Street. 'Anything happening?' I asked. 'Yes, plenty,' he said. 'Lot of stuff dropping farther east. Big fires in Queen Victoria Street, I'm told.' There were certainly big fires beginning somewhere beyond Ludgate Circus. Planes were zooming overhead all the time. I wondered what was happening to the Rodgers. Were they still in their shelter in Goldsmith Building? Used to go there in the early months of the blitz; we had joint suppers and played the gramophone. There was something reassuringly permanent about the outline of the Temple Church when we looked out or went out of the shelter. Even now, that idiotic *Nightingale sang in Berkeley Square* invariably reminds me of those nights in September 1940; it's made me almost love it. . . .

There was nobody in the shelter except Margaret Rodger, alone on a camp bed, reading a book, but looking very sorry for herself. She had been in bed with bronchitis for days; just her luck that Joe should be firewatching in the City that night, somewhere near London Bridge. Obviously a hot spot. She was worried about being unable to reach him on the phone. I said I hoped he had something better than a bowler hat to wear, and suggested she come to the office shelter for company; much safer as a shelter, too. Eventually she got ready and we went out. Behind the trees and the Temple Church the sky was bright red. And then I noticed that something serious was happening. The far end of the Temple Church was burning with the familiar greenish-white incendiary flame. I ran round the place, called and whistled, but couldn't see a soul. Where the hell were the wardens and the firewatchers of the Temple? Where was the fire-brigade?

I couldn't do anything myself, and the fire was now spreading rapidly. I looked for the cop, outside in Fleet Street. 'Can nothing be done about it? Don't you know the Temple Church is on fire?' 'Yes, I know,' he said dismally. 'I've notified the fire-brigade. But they aren't in the Temple. Don't know where they've gone. They ought to be along soon.' Didn't sound reassuring. There was hardly another soul in Fleet Street.

We hurried to the office. The women went down to the

shelter, and I decided to go and confer with the old boys. No sooner had I got up to the roof than I saw something fantastic. Five or six minutes at most could have passed since I had seen the beginning of the fire on the Temple Church. Now almost half the roof of the Church was blazing. To the left, Serjeant's Inn, with its central Grecian building, was burning furiously, flames leaping high into the sky. There were many other fires all round, but there was so much smoke, too, that there was no way of getting a clear idea of the number of fires a little farther off. They seemed to extend far to the East End, to the Surrey Side, and King's Cross. Only in the west there was nothing, and the floodlit Law Courts and St Dunstan's stood out clearly against a still, deep, blue-black sky. The outline of St Paul's could be seen from time to time, between the gusts of black smoke, but only dimly. Clearly, short of a full fire-brigade, nothing could save the Temple Church now. Up on the roof, the old boys had already put out two incendiaries and I asked them if they would like me to stay. Rather to my relief, they said no. They would ring the alarm bell for me if they wanted help. The lights on the stair had meantime gone out. I had no torch and had to strike matches to find my way down. There was stuff dropping all the time. Passing the lavatory on the third-floor landing I thought to myself : yes or no ? and decided no. Undignified to be killed in such an attitude. Still striking matches, I groped my way down to the shelter. It's a good shelter, well propped up with steel girders, but even so I couldn't help sitting up, listening. The two girls were there. It's very unpleasant to listen to bombs drop. And didn't they drop that night ! Clearly, the incendiary stage was over, and the Huns were now following it up with high explosives. Regularly, every two minutes, I should say, they came crashing down with the same tedious sickening whine. There was one crash which shook even this deep shelter. I felt unpleasantly sober and scared. However, after about an hour of this, the bombing became less regular. Marion now suggested going out and looking around. I thought I'd go to Paper Buildings to get my torch. We left Margaret in the shelter, asleep. She was running a temperature. It was about 3 o'clock.

The Temple Church was now a blazing torch. The conical dome had also caught fire. The top of Inner Temple Hall and of the Library was burning. But before we got to Paper Buildings

we met Harry the fat red-faced fireman. He and his pals had
just come from Upper Thames Street ; very bad fires there.
Their faces were grimy, and there was a futile, helpless look in
their eyes. 'See that?' said Harry, pointing to the roof of the
Library, 'just above our fire station. And we can't do nothing
about it. No bloody water.' 'Can't you get any from the
Thames?' ' No, it's low tide.' Didn't seem a good reason to
me ; but they knew better. 'All we can do,' said Harry,
'is to evacuate our fire station.' We offered to lend a hand, and
I couldn't help feeling a little annoyed that the firemen shouldn't
have anything better to do, and should look so helpless. But it
wasn't their fault, really. There must be something far wrong
with this much-vaunted alternative water supply they told the
Press about at the Ministry of Home Security the other day.

So down we went to the basement, and started carrying out
bedding and mattresses and top boots and whatnot. Dumped
them on and round a lorry outside. Whine . . . crash. . . .
Something was still dropping, not very far away. But the planes
now sounded like fighters. Odd there was so little gunfire all
night. Perhaps the night fighters were doing their stuff at last.
. . . We went on carrying bedding out of the fire station. Couldn't
move the steel bunks, though, nor the billiard table, nor the piano.
I remembered how, when passing the place in the afternoon, I
used to hear somebody playing bits of Bach and Chopin's 'rain-
drop' prelude. It was odd.

An irate-looking barrister now arrived at the fire station and
asked if I would lend a hand in the main part of Inner Temple
Library. We went in. The rafters of the roof were on fire. He
and another man climbed up a winding iron stair (used by the
librarians) carrying a red conical fire extinguisher. It was just
silly. It made a little fizzling noise, and that was all. The rafters
went on burning as before. I decided to go back to the fire station.
As I went out of the burning building I looked at the large oil
portraits of judges and barristers, all of them already badly
damaged by fire and water in December.

Marion, wearing a tin hat, had meantime been helping the
firemen to evacuate the rest of their possessions from the basement. I took her along to Paper Buildings, left her there, and
went back to the office. By this time a fire had started at the far
end of King's Bench Walk, near the Embankment. Up to the

roof again. Old Amos and Gibbins had just come back from a neighbouring roof, where they had put out an incendiary. All round, the fires were blazing more fiercely than ever. Immediately below us a row of small houses was spouting enormous flames, and burning rafters were collapsing with a crash every few minutes. Clearly, nothing could be done to save *these* houses. In the west, St Clement Danes was now burning, as if the h.e. damage it had suffered before wasn't enough. Curious how so many London buildings got it twice or three times. 'Dante's Inferno all right,' old Amos said, looking at the flaming panorama. A hot wind, mixed with burning débris, was blowing. The smoke hurt my eyes. The eyes of the two old boys were red and bloodshot, and Amos had a bruise below one eye ; something had hit him when one of the h.e.'s fell close-by. Stuff was still coming down, but I was too excited to feel scared. I asked if the two old boys would like me to take a turn, and let one of them have a rest, but they said no ; only would I, instead, lend a hand pumping water at the bank next door. Amos took me along there. Two girls had just been taken off in an ambulance, both badly injured. The bank had a private water supply from its own well ! Later I heard a shocking story from one of the men there ; but I haven't been able to check up on it yet. He said that when the people at the bank saw the fire starting on the Temple Church, they offered to put it out, but some warden said that the Temple fire brigade would arrive in due course. Isn't there some similar story about the Temple in the Great Fire of 1666, when the Temple people wouldn't allow any outsider to deal with the Temple fires ?

I went up on the roof of the bank and joined two AFS men who were working stirrup pumps from large buckets and playing the water on the wall of an adjoining building which was on fire. If we couldn't put the fire out, we could at least prevent its spreading to this building. It was infernally hot. Everything in front of us was blazing : the Temple Church, and the ruins of the Master's Lodge (it had been wrecked in January by an h.e.), and, beyond it, the Inner Temple Library, and, to the left, parts of Mitre Court, and Serjeant's Inn. Burning timber was crackling ; but I think one could *hear* the vast ring of fire itself breathing rhythmically, like a living thing. I think Wagner was right for once. A high wind was blowing clouds of black smoke and

burning débris. But when the wind abated, there was a continuous downpour of a golden rain of sparks. It was beautiful.
Clearly, something had gone seriously wrong. There was no
water in most places, if the fires had spread like this. . . .

It was about this time, I think, that the all-clear went, sound-
ing ironically over this hell of burning London. Fighters were
zooming overhead. Somebody arrived on the roof of the bank
and said he could relieve me. Through the rain of golden
sparks I went down to Fleet Street. Flat empty hoses were
stretched across the road, with mournful firemen looking on help-
lessly. Fires were burning in Chancery Lane, and, further east,
beyond Fetter Lane, enormous clouds of smoke were rising into
the sky. Yet Fleet Street itself seemed almost intact—except for
one big fire somewhere towards Ludgate Circus. It was about
5, or maybe 5.30. It had been light all night, and I had scarcely
noticed how daylight had come. . . .

I turned into Mitre Court. Good old Clachan—it was still
intact, though Serjeant's Inn to the left of it was burning furiously.
At this unusual hour the door of the pub was open. Great big
buxom Mrs Rothwell was there, with a few other people, looking
perturbed, but still discussing the situation in a business-like
manner. Her two cats were beside her. Old Rothwell had already
moved his personal belongings to some other place, and was now
preparing to go off to Earl's Court to see if the boss could send a
lorry to evacuate the pub itself. There was little time to lose, for
the fires were closing in on the old pub. The array of gin and
whisky bottles was faintly lit up by a solitary candle. The
windows were still blacked-out. An awful thought : what would
the newspaper gang and the AFS boys do if the Clachan disappeared ? It had become—till 10.30 every night—one of the few
places in Fleet Street where people went for company whenever
there was a raid on. I suggested that Mrs Rothwell should go
down to my rooms while Mr Rothwell was away looking for the
lorry. So I took her down there, complete with the two cats.

As I went back to Fleet Street I saw a woman going down
Mitre Court, carrying a bundle of clothes. I asked if I could
help. She said no, but would I help her husband, 'who's a cripple.'
He was following her, carrying two suitcases and more clothes.
They had been burned out of Serjeant's Inn. Carrying one of the
suitcases, I walked across to the Kardomah shelter with them,

next to St Dunstan's. We went through the sandbagged door, down to the shelter, which was crowded with burned-out people. 'Little Johnnie' the dwarf, who, wearing oversized striped trousers and spats, sells *Evening Standards* outside Mitre Court, was lying there huddled up on a bunk like a baby. 'Oh, Mr W,' he groaned, 'it was terrible.' He buried his head under the blanket. 'It's all right, Johnnie, you won't have to meet your Saviour this time through the unsolicited interference of that low cad Aydolf Hitler,' I said, repeating one of Johnnie's own ecclesiastical pomposities, which had made him quite popular in Fleet Street pubs for a while, till people got tired of him. 'Oh don't, Mr W,' he squealed, 'I am too upset to talk. Oh God, it was terrible ! I'm sure I'll be ill for weeks.' Johnnie is a great churchgoer, and enjoys the patronage of one or two parsons.

Here, down at the Kardomah shelter, was also the dignified old 'sergeant.' His wife was there, too. She was in tears. They had lost everything in their little house in Serjeant's Inn— even the wedding presents their daughter had recently received. I went along with him to see if he could retrieve anything. His face was grimy and drawn ; on it was a look of calamity. He was the housekeeper at Serjeant's Inn, and with the whole place burned out, his job had probably gone, too. Looking up Fetter Lane, I saw more large fires. I accompanied him through lanes of burning wreckage to Serjeant's Inn. The Grecian front of the main building stood out slender, like a piece of stage scenery, with nothing behind it. Everything had been burned out. The sergeant crawled down to the cellar of a house, the whole upper part of which was burning, and brought out a basket of a dozen eggs—apparently all he had saved. A cat was mewing on the cellar steps ; he spoke to it—called it 'poor old Jimmy,' or something. Carrying the basket to the Kardomah for him, I reflected that nothing could be baser than for me to run off with these eggs. Later, Mrs Rothwell said that the sergeant's wife had a special pride in life—her collection of brass candlesticks. All that was now gone.

Back to Paper Buildings. The two ends of King's Bench Walk were burning—the house nearest the Embankment—architecturally unimportant that one—and also one of the old houses, Number 2, I think, nearest to Mitre Court. Pity about it. But there was some water at last, and the firemen were now busy.

In Paper Buildings I found a whole crowd. Marion had returned there, after various adventures with burned-out people, Mrs Rothwell was there with her two cats, and, shortly before me, Joe and Margaret had arrived, Joe looking much the worse for wear and tear after his firewatching experiences in the City.

I looked incredibly dirty as I glanced into the mirror. Fortunately, there was still some water in the tap. There was no gas, but we made tea on the electric ring. Tea was welcome ; I felt as if I had eaten a ton of soot. Then, at 8 o'clock, I put on the news ; the theatre organ played the Toreador song, and then it, and the electric light—which had been flickering—died out. No news.

I felt desperately tired, but thought I'd have another look at the Temple. Joe came with me. The Church was a strange sight. The roof and dome had gone, but the stained-glass windows were brightly illuminated, as if a service were in progress inside. The beautiful porch and all the stonework were fortunately still standing, though much of it discoloured by the heat. The 1840 roof could, of course, be rebuilt. But, looking inside, I saw large pieces of the roof burning on the floor, and on top of the Crusaders' graves. Around the Church there were little pools of molten tin.

The firemen were now pouring hundreds of gallons into the roaring furnace of the Inner Temple Hall. The air was thick with smoke, there was a black haze over everything, and burning fragments were flying in the wind, and the sun was a dark-red disc.

Then I saw a little smoke emerging from one corner of the old brick building above the Wren Cloisters. Joe and I went up the rickety wooden stairs—the whole fabric had been so badly shattered by an h.e. in November that the building was now uninhabited—got up to the top flat, which was empty, and found our way on to the roof, up an insecure, rusty old stepladder. We carried some buckets of sand and a shovel—not much use, I admit. We crawled along the edge of the roof, holding on to uneven soot-covered old tiles. From one attic window came a gust of acrid smoke ; otherwise the fire did not seem to have gone very far. As on all fours I crawled past the window I held my breath. It occurred to me how easy it must be to be overcome by smoke, and how painless to be 'burned alive.' Crawled back along the roof and then hurried downstairs—for sand alone was no use. The firemen were still pouring the precious water into the wreck of the Library. We argued with them that the Cloisters were far more important to save—for if they went, the whole of Pump Court would go. They agreed, and began to play their hose on the Cloister building. But two minutes later the flames burst through the roof, and the wooden fabric of the house went up in flames. Five minutes from the time we had been on the roof it was blazing like a cigarette carton. Lamb Building, between the Library and the Church, was still intact, however. I looked almost spitefully at it. Silly square box, I said to myself —wish it had burned instead.

I went home. Everybody had gone, but Mrs Rothwell was still there with her cats. I reported to her one of the firemen's views that, with the water supply improving, they would manage to save the Clachan. She was sceptical. There was a knock at the door ; a policeman had come to fetch the doctor from next door. In Temple Avenue a man had his legs pinned under wreckage. The other man was dead ; but this one, after being unconscious, was now in great pain. The doctor went out. He had been at Blackfriars all night attending to casualties, and was jovially gruesome about the whole thing.

I got to sleep in the end. I woke up about one, still feeling rather tired and hungry. Mrs Rothwell had gone. I went along Mitre Court, was glad that the firemen seemed to have got the fire under control. Fat Harry and the tall lanky AFS fellow with the bad teeth were there, the latter in his Sunday best. He had been off duty, he informed me with a touch of joviality. The others hoped they would get off work from 4 to 10 to get some sleep. The station had been burned out ; they were moving into Paper Buildings.

At the office old Amos had not had any food since yesterday ; so I went home and fetched him what food I had.

I couldn't get any conveyance along Fleet Street ; so I walked to Aldwych. St Clement Danes—nothing left but a shell, the little black statue of Dr Johnson was all right, though. Got a bus near Wellington Street for Oxford Circus. The Strand hadn't suffered at all, nor Piccadilly Circus, nor Regent Street. . . . Everything looked very normal. I even got a newspaper. I had lunch at one of those new 'Inn' places—only cold salmon and tea ; there was no gas. The place was crowded and people were looking as though nothing much had happened. I was supposed to go to the Free French Joan of Arc celebrations that morning, but what was the good? Should I go to the de Gaulle H.Q. now? No, too lazy. Went back by bus to Fleet Street. Got out at the Temple.

What a sight it was! Nothing but a shell was left of the Cloisters, most of Pump Court had also gone, and then I suddenly saw Lamb Building. It also had been completely burned out: the left half of the front had collapsed ; the left and right walls were standing up at a dangerous angle ; the whole thing was cracked in every direction. The golden lamb over the doorway alone looked normal, and a bit of the stair—leading into emptiness a few feet up. The great bomb of January 2 must have badly shattered the 300-year-old brick walls to make them collapse like this. Along the chimney stack could still be seen the fireplaces.

Well, it was just part of the fun. But to think that it was quite intact at 9 and gone now seemed absurd. It was not adjoining anything, and there had been water after 9. Could nothing have been done?

On to the office at 5. There was no light, and all the telephone wires had gone to blazes. The chief sub, who had watched the fires from Muswell Hill, looked gloomy. The Assistant Editor arrived with a very business-like air. We all moved to another office in Tudor Street. Gas mains were blazing in Whitefriars Street ; there was a stink of gas, and police notices all over the place : 'Gas Danger : No Smoking.'

I wrote a short piece complaining of the shortage of fire-watchers, and of the inadequacy of the emergency water supply. I went home at 8, for there was nothing else to do at the office. To bed early. There was a warning, but nothing much happened. I wanted a bath, but there was no gas.

This morning—Monday—I got up late. The papers announced—first news to me, for the wireless was off all the time (oh, no, it was casually mentioned in the office yesterday)—that the House of Commons had been blitzed to hell, and Westminster Abbey damaged.

Went out to lunch. The ruins of Serjeant's Inn were still burning. Of course, Emile's was shut, though Emile was outside. On Saturday he had spent an infernal night on the roof, putting out incendiaries. The Geographia place next to the *Glasgow Herald* was completely burned out. Fleet Street was still a mess, and mobs of sightseers were still strolling around, much to the annoyance of the firemen and repair squads. There were hoses all over the place, and a stink of gas. Couldn't think where to get lunch. Luckily I met Charles Gombault, who suggested Reuter's canteen. He said that Russia had just recognised the rebel Iraq Government. At the canteen I ran into Andy Rothstein, who defended Russia's decision very feebly. 'You didn't recognise the incorporation of the Baltic States,' etc. etc. Looked out of the window from the top of Reuter's. Most of the houses round Ludgate Circus were just shells. St Paul's was still standing, though. Ate some cold meat and pickles and mashed.

Later I went for a walk along Fetter Lane, and through Cursitor Street and Shoe Lane up to Holborn. Nearly every house was burned out. Whole streets of nothing but smouldering skeletons. A tract of London between Holborn and Fleet Street, except for the big office blocks in Fleet Street itself, must be pretty well wiped out. It might be a good idea to build through it an east-west artery, linking up St Paul's with Piccadilly. Funny, there was so much smoke around the office on Saturday night there was just no way of finding out what was and wasn't burning.

Back to the Temple. At the Tudor Street Gate I met Mr Houghton, the venerable old porter with his bowler hat. He had been a Temple porter for 42 years, and he was 75 now. He told me he had put out a lot of incendiaries in the Temple Gardens that night. I took him for a drink to the Temple pub. There were two firewatchers from the Temple there, and three sailors, who sang, 'Isn't it a lovely day to be caught in the *raid* ?'

OPENING THE TIMES I saw, 'Hitler's deputy in Britain.' Didn't believe my eyes. What rubbish ! Then I saw that Hess had landed near Glasgow by parachute on Saturday night. Couldn't make head or tail of it at first.

TUESDAY
MAY 13

Looks like an anti-Russian move, and like an attempt to confuse America and to prevent her from entering the war. How silly : the *News Chronicle* describes Hess as 'the only honest Nazi,' or words to that effect. As if an honest Nazi wasn't a contradiction in terms, like an honourable white-slave trafficker.

WROTE A PIECE about the ARP scandal, particularly the lack of mobile canteens throughout Saturday night, at least in this part of London. Many of the firemen in Queen Victoria Street worked for 13 hours in fire and smoke without even a cup of tea. No wonder they are fed-up. Also, the whole question of AFS pensions and compensation needs a thorough overhaul.

BY THE WAY, in the Temple yesterday I ran into old Dickson; his office off Pump Court has been burned out. He agreed with me that the firewatching in the Temple was quite inadequate. In Middle Temple Lane I heard a barrister complaining that the delayed action bomb hadn't been moved yet. 'The Yids of Park Lane always get priority,' he said. Maybe he is right, but still, why doesn't he go and pick up the damned bomb himself? I am sick of seeing all these people mooching about the Temple and holding up their arms in holy horror at Hitler's wickedness. A fat lot they did on Saturday to stop the Temple from being burned down. Most of them were away for the week-end.

I rang up H. at the Ministry of Home Security and asked why the water supply had broken down so badly on Saturday. He said the mains were smashed and also there was low tide on the Thames. Why should that matter? He couldn't really produce an adequate explanation. Said that in any case substitute water supplies were never the same as the real thing. Further, fire brigades can't very well rush from one place to another. On Saturday they had to concentrate on the three worst places— in Queen Victoria Street ; just behind Liverpool Street station ; and at the Elephant and Castle. Regarding the Elephant, Mrs Tall, the charlady who lives in Bermondsey, said this morning that it was quite unrecognisable.

WHAT A TEDIOUS JOB staying up here in the office to firewatch when there is nothing to watch. It is raining heavily.

I have just been on the roof, and though it is nearly full moon, one can hardly see a thing—
WEDNESDAY
MAY 14
except a faint glow of a fire still burning since Saturday, somewhere off Queen Victoria Street. I am sitting up here on the third floor with no light but a candle. Downstairs, in the subs' room, they have somehow managed to keep one bulb going.

THIS MORNING the man from the dairy in Fetter Lane arrived, to explain that they had been burned out, together with my food coupons ; quite a problem. . . .

AS I WENT OUT, I ran into the crowd of AFS boys, among them a new one, good-looking and very Eton-and-Oxford. Said he had 'read me for years' in the *New Statesman*. He seemed a little out of place with our Harrys and Dicks and their rough-and-tumble ways.

One of the fellows in our office had one of his two sisters killed on Saturday.

BOB, WHO WAS AWAY for the week-end, got a fit of cold feet when he came back. So he has decided to move out of his house as soon as possible. His wife mustn't stay another night in London, he said. She *must* get the 6.55 train at Paddington *at the latest* every night ; and the nights he *has* to be in London he will probably sleep in his office shelter. Yesterday I pulled his leg about 'you week-enders who let London be burned out.' He half-resented it but made no effort to justify himself.

MARION TO-DAY took me down to the canteen in Borough High Street where she works. We took a taxi, which went in strange circles via Waterloo Bridge—one-way only. The new damage in Borough High Street, in addition to that caused already by h.e.'s a few weeks ago, is pretty terrible and when, walking along rows of shattered small houses and shops, we got to No. 96, there wasn't any there. Just a heap of rubble—direct hit. Farther along, past the church, another house had been completely demolished. Two women were standing above the heap of rubble watching ARP men extricating odds and ends ; with them was a tiny blue-eyed baby, in a sort of wooden box on wheels. It looked half-witted and kept wagging its head from side to side like a pendulum. Must have been bomb-shock or something.

Took tram back to Blackfriars. Blackfriars Road mostly a shambles. Yet, looking west from Blackfriars Bridge everything seemed extraordinarily normal ; only, with this fireblitz, which leaves walls of houses intact, it's all very deceptive. . . .

This last Saturday blitz was probably the most destructive of the lot—as bad as the December 29 blitz, and with far more casualties. God, it's boring being up here. I have sent old Gibbins to bed ; and I shan't waken him till 3 or 4 o'clock.

THE MINISTRY OF HOME SECURITY yesterday told me that the water mains—or most of them—had by now been repaired, and that there is no danger of London being without water if there's another raid. Weren't the Germans fools not to have followed up Saturday's blitz with one on Sunday ? Probably they just couldn't do it—at least not on a big scale . . . especially after losing 33 planes in one night. There's never been anything like it. From the point of view of the war this first real triumph of the night-fighters is the really big 'angle' of May 10.

Voigt, looking like a 50-year-old baby, blew into the office. His theory is that Hess is insane. Tripe.

Earlier to-night we went to the Clachan. At night, by candle-light (so old McBayne said) it looked just as pubs looked in the days of Dr Johnson. McBayne worries much more about places than about people. George once remarked, 'Old Mac will go on moaning over Wren churches ; it's all Wren churches with him. What worries *me* is the women and the kiddies who get killed or lose their homes.'

However, hereabouts we're getting more or less back to normal. Buses aren't running yet, but there's already a lot of traffic. This afternoon two fire-engines dashed down Fleet Street ringing their bells like mad. A dormant fire must have started up again.

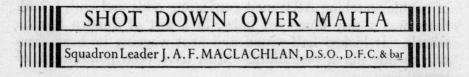

SHOT DOWN OVER MALTA

Squadron Leader J. A. F. MACLACHLAN, D.S.O., D.F.C. & bar

[*When the incidents described here took place,* SQUADRON LEADER MACLACHLAN *was 22. As an officer of the regular Air Force he went to France immediately on the outbreak of war, and there, flying with great distinction, earned himself the D.F.C. and bar. After he was shot down over Malta, losing an arm, he came back to England and was fitted with a specially devised artificial arm that enabled him to operate the controls of an aircraft. He became the leader of a night-fighter squadron. As an intruder specialist he had a spectacular period of success during the spring and summer of 1942, shooting down many enemy aircraft by night. To his D.F.C. was added the D.S.O. and the highest award of the Czech Air Force. He was also the originator of the train-wrecking campaign that has now become a regular part of Fighter Command's work over the North of France. In the first month of its operations against trains his squadron destroyed fifty engines, frequently putting large sections of the Paris—Rouen—Dieppe system out of action.* MACLACHLAN *is tall and fair ; temperamentally exuberant, friendly, part Scots, part New Zealander. The exact quality of his passion for flying and his determination to overcome a great physical handicap are best seen in these extracts from his diary.*]

No sooner had I taken over my machine on the evening of the 8th than all fighters were ordered to scramble. We screeched up to 16,000 ft. (all six of us), but as it was almost dark by then we split up and each stayed at a separate height, mine being 16,000 ft. Two or three raiders came in and dropped their bombs without being picked up, but at about 7.10 I saw one beautifully illuminated at about 10,000 ft. over Rabat. I pulled the plug and went screaming after it, catching it as it was just going out of range of the searchlights. I could see it quite clearly in the moonlight, so closed till it completely filled my reflector sight. The rear gunner must have seen me coming, for he opened fire at the same moment as I did. As soon as I pressed my firing button I was blinded by the flames from my guns, so, fearing I might ram him in the dark, I ceased firing to get my bearings again. I thought for a moment that he was on fire, flames and sparks seemed to be pouring from his fuselage. Then to my horror I realised that the flames were coming from the muzzles of his rear guns, and the sparks were tracer and incendiary bullets, streaming back unpleasantly close to my head. For some unknown reason I always feel that no one can hit me when I am firing at them, so, with eight guns blazing, I closed to about 50 yds., and again ceased fire to take stock of my surroundings. This time there was no return fire from the bomber. All I could see was its dark sil-

FEBRUARY 10, 1941

E

houette against the moonlit sky, and the pale glow from its ex-hausts. I realised the fight was as good as won, so taking careful aim at very close range, I fired a fairly long burst. Incendiary bullets poured into the helpless bomber, but it did not catch fire. I was blinded by smoke and oil, so broke away slightly to see what had happened. A long trail of smoke streamed out behind the bomber, but it did not seem to be losing height. I finished off my ammo in an attack from the rear starboard quarter, but with no apparent results. A feeling of helpless frustration came over me. A few moments before I had been certain of getting him, but now I was not so sure. I glanced at my instruments and saw I was only doing 160 m.p.h. and going down at 1000 ft. min. Perhaps I had got him after all! I looked at my instruments again to make sure, and saw I was down to 5000 ft. When I took my head out of the cockpit the bomber had vanished. I circled round for a little but could not find it again, so returned and landed. H.Q. later confirmed that this aircraft crashed into the sea.

No sooner had I landed than Eliot took off and patrolled the dead area for about an hour, unfortunately without result. Immediately he had landed I again took off and climbed up to 16,000 ft. over Filfla. I had been on patrol for about a quarter of an hour when the searchlights came on and formed a fairly concentrated intersection over Luca. I immediately turned towards it, and to my delight saw an 88 beautifully illuminated at about 10,000 ft. slowly turning north. My mouth started to water as I opened the throttle, pulled the plug, and lowered my seat. By the time I had turned on my reflector sight and put my gun-firing switch in the firing position, I was doing about 340 m.p.h. and slowly closing on the bomber. The tension was terrific. For what seemed like minutes the bomber hung there in front of me, shining tantalisingly in the searchlights. My mouth watered and my heart beat furiously as I watched its wings slowly growing in my sights. I could feel my aircraft rocking in its slip-stream, and with great difficulty overcame my natural impulse to open fire. At last its wings completely filled my sights, and aiming at the top of the fuselage I let fly. This time I was ready for the blinding flames from my guns, and after a two-seconds' burst I ceased fire to see what had happened. The 88, which was still about 150 yds. in front of me, was doing a gentle turn to the left. I could see quite a lot of the upper surface of its wings and fuselage, so aiming about a length in front I gave it a five- or six-second squirt. Clouds of smoke came back, and my cockpit was filled with the smell of burning aeroplane. I turned to one side to avoid hitting the Jerry, and was immediately picked up by our searchlights. By the time I had extricated myself from these, my target had vanished. I felt almost sure I had got it, so called up ground control and asked if they could confirm its destruction. Five minutes later they called me back and said that some soldiers had seen it crash into the sea.

As I still had about one-third of my ammo left I stayed on patrol for another half-hour, but the searchlights failed to pick anything up, so I landed without further excitement. As I taxied back to the dispersal point Eliot took off past me. I watched the red glow of his exhausts disappear into the night sky, and then stopped my engine. Hardly had I got out of my kite when the searchlights went on again and after a few minutes picked up a Jerry which they held right across the Island. Unfortunately Chubby had not had time to climb high enough to catch it, so it got clean away. About half an hour later they picked up another, but for some unknown reason lost it again before Chubby had time to close. The poor boy honestly does have the most appalling luck.

Eventually Chubby landed and I again took off, climbing to 17,000 ft. over Filfla. Two Jerries came in but were not picked up, then a third approached the Island and was picked up just before it crossed the coast on its way home. I screeched after it, but the searchlights lost it long before I was within range. I followed it out towards Sicily but could see no trace of it, so returned to the dead area. After patrolling for another half hour, I landed without further incident.

Chubby then went up for an hour, followed again by myself, but on neither trip did the searchlights manage to illuminate anything. At about 3.0 a.m. the all clear went, so, feeling completely exhausted, we tumbled into the ambulance and slept like logs till we were awakened at dawn by the early morning watch who took over from us. Altogether I did 4.25 hrs. flying.

I HAVE BEEN OFF FLYING for the last two days as I have had a very painful stye in my left eye. It has been much better today however, and this morning I took a Hurricane up and did about half an hour's aerobatics which I greatly enjoyed.

FEBRUARY
11

This afternoon 'B' flight were up at 20,000 ft. when they were attacked by ME 109's. Bradbury, Watson, Thacker and Pain went in to attack three JU 88's and were immediately set on. Watson and Thacker were shot down in the sea, and old Brad, though shot to hell, managed to get back and land at Luca. His kite was riddled with cannon and bullet holes ; all the fabric was torn off one side, and his rudder control was shot away except for one strand of wire on one side.

Thacker managed to bale out and was picked up by an R.A.F. speed-boat, after being in the sea for about an hour. Poor old Watson was never found.

The appearance of 109's has greatly shaken the morale of the Squadron (and mine in particular). I think that the sooner we hack some down the better.

I am on night standby tonight, and as the weather is perfect I think we shall have some track. I certainly hope so.

LAST TUESDAY NIGHT I had two scrambles but on neither of them did the searchlights manage to illuminate anything. This afternoon I saw 109's myself ; I was leading 'A' flight south of Comino, at about 22,000 ft., when I saw four 109's coming straight towards me. I was up sun of them, and they did not see me until we were only about 1000 yards apart. We were in sections line astern, and for once in really decent formation. We evidently looked 'très formidable' for as soon as Jerry saw us he broke formation and, turning steeply to starboard, climbed away from us in a shambles. Our poor old Hurrybirds were no match for the 109's and though we chased them with throttles wide open they just left us standing. For the rest of the patrol I suffered acute twitch, but by the grace of God we were not attacked.

This evening there have been great discussions in the Mess as to the best way to deal with 109's.

AS 'A' FLIGHT were on the 9 o'clock watch John decided to have all the bloodthirsty pilots on, in the hopes of getting a 109. We arranged that if we were attacked we would break away and form a defensive circle.

FEBRUARY 16

At about 9.15 we were ordered to scramble, and climbed to 20,000 ft. We were still climbing over Luca when six ME 109's screamed down on us from out of the sun. We immediately broke away and formed up a rather wide circle. Just as I took my place in the circle I saw four more Messerschmitts coming down out of the sun. I turned back under them, and they all overshot me. I looked round very carefully but could see nothing, so turned back on to the tail of the nearest Hun, who was chasing some Hurricanes in front of him. We were all turning gently to port so I cut the corner and was slowly closing on the Hun. I was determined to get him, and must have been concentrating so intently on his movements that, like a fool, I forgot to look in the mirror until it was too late. Suddenly there was a crash in my cockpit—bits and pieces seemed to fly everywhere. Instinctively I went into a steep spiral dive, furiously angry that I had been beaten at my own game. My left arm was dripping with blood, and when I tried to raise it only the top part moved, the rest hung limply by my side. Everything happened so quickly that I have no very clear recollection of what actually took place. I remember opening my hood, disconnecting my oxygen and R T connections and standing up in the cockpit. The next thing I saw was my kite diving away from me, the roar of its engine gradually fading as it plunged earthwards. It was a marvellous feeling to be safely out of it, everything seemed so quiet and peaceful. I could clearly hear the roar of engines above me, and distinctly heard one long burst of cannon fire. I could not see what was happening as I was falling upsidedown and my legs obscured all view of the aircraft above me. My arm was beginning to hurt pretty badly, so I decided to pull my chute straight-away in case I fainted from loss of blood. I reached round for my ripcord but could not find it. For some unknown reason I thought my chute must have been torn off me while I was getting out of my kite, and almost gave up making any further efforts to save myself. I remember thinking that the whole process of being shot down and being killed seemed very much simpler and less horrible than I had always imagined. There was just going to be

one big thud when I hit the deck and then all would be over—my
arm would stop hurting and no more 109's could make dirty
passes at me behind my back. I think I must have been gradually
going off into a faint when I suddenly thought of mother reading
the telegram saying that I had been killed in action. I made one
last effort to see if my parachute was still there, and to my amaze-
ment and relief found it had not been torn off after all. With
another supreme effort I reached round and pulled the ripcord.
There was a sickening lurch as my chute opened and my harness
tightened round me so that I could hardly breathe. I felt horribly
ill and faint. Blood from my arm came streaming back into my
face, in spite of the fact that I was holding the stump as tightly as I
could. I was able to breathe only with the utmost difficulty,
and my arm hurt like hell. I could see Malta spread out like a
map 15,000 ft. below me, and I longed to be down there—just
to lie still and die peacefully. I was woken from this stupor by
the roar of an engine, and naturally thought some bloodthirsty
Jerry had come to finish me off. I don't think I really minded
what happened, though certainly the thought of a few more
cannon shells flying past me didn't exactly cheer me up. To my
joy, however, I saw that my escort was a Hurricane, piloted, as I
learned later, by Eric Taylor. He had quite rightly decided that
he could do no good by playing with the Huns at 20,000 ft.,
so came down to see that none of them got me.

For what seemed like hours I hung there, apparently motion-
less, with Malta still as far away as ever. Once or twice I started
swinging very badly, but as I was using my only hand to stop
myself bleeding to death, I was unable to do anything about it.
At approximately 1500 ft. I opened my eyes again and to my
joy realised that I was very much lower down. For a little I was
afraid I was going to land in the middle of a town, but I mercifully
drifted to the edge of this. For the last 100 ft. I seemed to drop
out of the sky—the flat roof of a house came rushing up at me,
and just as I was about to land on it, it dodged to one side and I
ended up in a little patch of green wheat. I hit the ground with a
terrific thud, rolled over once or twice, and then lay back intending
to die quietly. This, however, was not to be. Scarcely had I
got myself fairly comfortable and closed my eyes when I heard the
sound of people running. I hurriedly tried to think up some
famous last words to give my public, but never had a chance to

utter them. I was surrounded by a crowd of shouting, gesticulating Malts, who pulled at my parachute, lifted my head and drove me so furious that I had to give up the dying idea in order to concentrate completely on kicking every Malt who came within range. (From what the soldiers told me after, I believe I registered some rather effective shots.)

Eventually two very dim stretcher bearers arrived with a first aid outfit. I told them to put a tourniquet on my arm and give me some morphia, whereupon one of them started to bandage my wrist and the other went off to ask what morphia was. In the end I got them to give me the first aid outfit and fixed myself up. At last a doctor arrived who actually knew what to do. He put me on a stretcher, had me carried about half a mile across fields to an ambulance, which in turn took me down to the local advanced field dressing station. Here they filled me with morphia, gave me ether, and put my arm in a rough splint. When I came round they gave me a large tot of whiskey, another injection of morphia and sent me off to Imtarfa, as drunk as a lord. When I eventually arrived at the hospital I was feeling in the best of spirits and apparently shook the sisters by asking them to bring on the dancing girls.

They wasted no time in getting me up to the theatre, and after making the General promise not to take my arm off I gave a running commentary as the ether took effect.

When I came round I was back in M.3 surrounded by screens, with Sister Dempsey sitting in a chair beside me. After a quick glance I was delighted to see that my arm was still there, so went off to sleep again, feeling very cheerful about the whole thing. The next two days were pretty average mental and physical hell—thank God I cannot remember very much about them. I was having a saline transfusion day and night, and unfortunately my blood kept clotting, which necessitated making fresh holes in my arm and legs. I remember watching the saline solution dripping down the glass tube from the container—terrified that the drips were becoming less frequent and would eventually stop again.

Everyone was simply wizard to me, especially Sister Dempsey. She used to sit by my bed for hours when she was off duty. I got a lot of secret amusement telling her to leave me as I wanted to die. She would get really worried and stroke my forehead and plead with me not to talk about dying. Had she but known it I had already made up my mind to get better, and nothing in the world was further from my thoughts than death.

As these first two days dragged on I began to realise that there was no hope of saving my arm. The blood circulation was all right, but my finger movement was scarcely visible, and I could hardly feel anything in my hand. My whole arm began to smell positively revolting, and the pain was almost unbearable. Davidson and the General kept hinting that I would be much better off without it, but I was terrified that without it I should never be able to fly again, so refused to let them touch it. By the third morning, however, I was so weak and the pain so unbearable that they had little difficulty in taking me up to the theatre and performing the necessary operation.

When I came to I was in the cabin at the end of M.3. and still having a saline transfusion. As I can remember very little about the rest of the day I presume that I must have been unconscious most of the time.

THIS MORNING I was moved back into the ward as I am now off the danger list. Just before lunch today a Macchi pilot whom I shot down on January 9 was wheeled in, and is now in the next bed to me. His arm is still very bad though the bullet wound in his thigh has healed. I think he was even more surprised to see me than I was to see him. It certainly is a crazy war.

FEBRUARY 20

There is a wizard set of chaps here. Opposite me is a Lieutenant Going, R.N., commonly known as the General, who is the life and soul of the party. He was in the *Illustrious* when she was bombed, and had his right leg blown off, and the rest of him pretty well filled with shrapnel.

Next to him is a Lieutenant who was also in *Illustrious*. The poor boy goes through hell every day when his dressings are done, but is very cheerful about the whole thing. On my left is an extraordinarily decent W/O who has a leg and an arm broken and is fixed up with a marvellous set of weights and pulleys.

After looking round at these chaps I'm beginning to feel almost well again. With any luck I should be out of here long before most of them.

I AM REALLY BEGINNING to feel a little better, though I still have morphia at night.   Yesterday Ginger O'Sullivan came to see me and says he has written to mother.   I hope he hasn't told her I've lost my arm.   This afternoon Chubby and Terry Foxton came up and gave me all the Squadron news. Everyone else got back O.K. when I was shot down, but McAdam's kite was just about shot to pieces.   Langdon, who saw me being shot down, says that as soon as I turned back after the 109's two more came down out of the sun on to my tail.   They were going at well over 400 m.p.h. but the first managed to get in a quick squirt before he overshot me.

FEBRUARY 22

Yesterday a formation of the DO. 215's came over and Hamilton got one, and the rest of the boys shaved another.   One or two of them collected the add rear-gun bullet but no one was seriously damaged.

This evening I had an extremely interesting conversation with Macchi about the performances of various Italian aircraft.   He says he was flying C.R. 32's in the Spanish war and then went over to 42's, which he much prefers to Macchis.   Incidentally his proper name is Luigi Allimino.   He is really a charming fellow, and very interesting to talk to.

I AM REALLY FEELING very much better now though I get a lot of pain at night.   The piece of shrapnel that was touching the nerve in my ankle is apparently working its way to the surface, as I can now walk without any pain.

FEBRUARY 25

Yesterday morning there was a wizard scrap at about 3000 ft. over Tintarfa.   The Hurricanes were on patrol in the usual sections in V formation when down came about four 109's at a simply phenomenal speed.   The Hurricanes did a very spectacular breakaway, Sgt. Bamburger coming down in a spin, and the 109's disappeared into the sun again.   One of our kites got separated from the rest and was immediately set on by a 109.   As usual the Hun came screaming in at about 400 m.p.h. and got in about a 2-seconds' burst before he had to break away to avoid overshooting.   He must have been a rotten shot for in spite of the fact that he closed to about 50 yards he never hit the

Hurricane once. The pilot, Sgt. Davidson, apparently knew nothing about it until he saw the Jerry breaking away, and then it was too late to do anything in the way of a counter-attack. There were several other rather shaky-do's, but no one got badly shot up.

TODAY WE HAD one of the biggest, if not the biggest, blitzes ever experienced. At about 13.00 hrs. the alarm went, and eight Hurricanes led by Eric Taylor roared off FEBRUARY into the blue. They had reached about 28,000 ft. 26 (hoping to catch the 109's) when a terrific formation of 87's came in at about 10,000 ft. As usual the A.A. guns opened up and the first machine to dive went straight into the road at Luca, without ever releasing its bombs. The Hurricanes, who started to come down as soon as they saw the A.A. fire, were now at about 10,000 ft. just south of Luca. As the Junkers pulled out of their dives and emerged from the barrage they were immediately set on by the Hurricanes, who were in turn attacked by 109's. This evolved into a series of little processions which, led by 87's, all headed south towards Filfla. On two occasions I saw an 87, a Hurricane, and a 109 in almost perfect line astern formation all pumping lead into each other. After the 87's came a large composite formation of 88's, DO. 215's, and HE. 111's all escorted by ME. 110's and Macchis. None or very few of these ventured below 6000 or 8000 ft. and as the Hurricanes were all below 3000 ft. they were pretty safe. The A.A., however, got an 88 which dived vertically into the sea from about ten Grand, making a row like the souls awakening. The whole attack was directed against Luca, and by the time the last Jerries arrived the column of smoke and dust had risen to about 4000 ft. and completely obscured the north-east end of the Island. As the last Jerries flew off the Hurricanes, most of whom had expended all their ammunition, returned one by one and circled Ta-Kali. Suddenly one of them started smoking and looked as if it would burst into flames at any moment. It went into a shallow dive and finally disappeared behind a hill. I heard later that the pilot was Terry Foxton, and that somehow he managed to crash land it on Ta-Kali, writing the kite off. but escaping unhurt himself. He had apparently been hit in the radiator and his engine seized up.

This raid has, I'm afraid, been highly successful from Jerry's point of view. Six Wimpies were burnt out and all the others put U/S by bomb splinters. The hangars are smashed. It cost him 14 planes definitely destroyed and several probables. Our losses were four Hurricanes and three pilots, one of whom was poor Eric Taylor. He was last seen chasing an 87 with a 109 on his tail. Later on his Mae West was washed up with a cannon hole right through the chest—he certainly couldn't have known much about it. Langdon and Kersey were the other two casualties. Young Eliot got his first Hun since he's been here—a flaming 87 and another probable. Terry Foxton also got a cert and a probable before he was shot down. Sgt. Robinson got a 109—the first to be shot down in Malta. Altogether a most exciting day.

THIS AFTERNOON I got up and dressed for the first time. I managed all right except for my tie, which I eventually managed to do by holding one end in the drawer of the dressing-table, and so keeping it tight while I tied the knot. I feel pretty shaky on my feet, and get pins and needles in my arm if I move about too quickly.

FEBRUARY
27

This morning Macchi had his arm operated on again, and has been feeling pretty bad all day. He really is damn brave about it, and hardly ever makes much noise. He stuffs his mouth full of blanket and bites that when his arm hurts very badly. It makes me feel terrible to see him going through so much pain and know I am responsible. Lying here and seeing all these mutilated chaps makes me realise more than ever how utterly mad this war is.

This evening I went through to M.4 and had a game of poker with Wyatt Smith and a Maltese Naval officer. I made 6s.

Sister O'Connell and Peggy Lane are on night duty, and we have great fun ragging them when they come round in the evening. I sleep without morphia now and can even lie on my left side if I arrange the pillows properly.

THIS AFTERNOON I got up after lunch, and had just finished dressing when Hammond arrived in Jock's car. I got permission from the Sister to go for a short walk and then drove the car down to the dispersal points. I find I can manage quite well, though of course there is very little traffic on the road. When I arrived at the bus I saw the A.O.C.'s staff car and our brake. On closer inspection I saw to my surprise and secret joy that I had run into a Sunday luncheon party. I was greeted with surprise by Ginger, who introduced me to Lady Strickland. The A.O.C. then emerged from a Hurricane and was amazed to see me up so soon. Needless to say, I shot them a pretty good line. At last I was able to transfer my attention to the boys. They were equally astonished to see me, as none of them knew I had been allowed up.

FEBRUARY
28

This morning Jock Barber was up with 'A' flight when they ran into four 110's. Everyone seems to have squirted everyone else but without any results. Apparently Jock and the boys came round a cloud one way and the Messerschmitts came round the other. Although Jerry passed within 50 yards both parties were so surprised that neither had time to have a decent squirt at the other.

I had tea in the Mess and went back to Tintarfa at about 6 p.m. No one had missed me so I hopped into bed feeling very pleased with myself.

I FELT VERY TIRED after last Sunday's excursion and have consequently been taking it easy for the last two days. This morning Chubby came up for me in Jock's car and I drove down to the Mess, where I had lunch. In the afternoon we went into Valetta in John's car. I did a spot of shopping, after which we went to see Dorothy Lamour in *Jungle Princess*. Just before the show finished the air raid warning went, and a few minutes later the guns opened up. We stayed in the cinema for a little, but as the guns went on firing we decided there must be a bit of a blitz on, so went out to see what was happening. . . . As we emerged at the top of Merchant Street we heard the roar of engines and saw a 109 dive down and attack a Hurricane at

MARCH
3

about 1500 ft. over Grand Harbour. Just as the attacking
Messerschmitt opened fire the Hurricane pulled up into a vertical
climb and I saw, for the first time, another 109 flying just above
the Hurricane. The attacking Messerschmitt was going far too
fast to follow the Hurricane and apparently missed it altogether.
Our kite, however, opened fire on the second 109 while still in
a vertical climb, then, keeping its sights on, it half rolled out on
to the tail of the Messerschmitt, firing all the time. The whole
manœuvre was marvellous to watch—certainly some of the best
flying I have seen in this Squadron. Unfortunately Jerry was too
well armoured to fall victim to what must have been a rather
inaccurate attack.

YESTERDAY I hitch-hiked down to Ta-Kali hoping to fly
the Maggy. Unfortunately it was U/S, so I had to content myself
with lunch in the Mess and a game of poker in the
MARCH   afternoon.
5   Today, however, I was more fortunate. Chubby
came up for me just before lunch, and in the afternoon I did my first flight since I was shot down. Exactly fifteen
days since my arm was amputated. Chubby did a circuit and
bump first, then I did one, during which I shot up Tintarfa
Hospital, flying past M.3 with my wingtip not more than ten
feet from the windows. It shook the sister, but not nearly as
much as it shook me! After I had done two or three satisfactory
landings Chubby got out and I did about 20 minutes' solo flying,
during which I went and had a look at the field where I landed by
parachute. I can't describe the marvellous feeling of satisfaction
that I get from flying again. During my first few days in hospital
I went through untold mental agony—fearing I should never be
able to go back to the old game. Now that I can cope I'll fight
Heaven and earth to get back on to fighters again. My one
ambition now is to get a 109, and God willing I'll do it. When I
arrived back in M.3 I found a letter from mother and the shilling
bet I had won from Sister Dempsey by flying within three weeks
of my accident. I certainly am a happy man tonight.

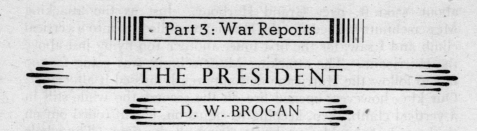

THE PRESIDENT

D. W. BROGAN

When Woodrow Wilson declared that making the world safe for democracy was a primary war aim, G. K. Chesterton remarked that the world would never be made safe for democracy since it is 'a dangerous trade.' How dangerous, neither Wilson nor Chesterton could possibly have realised in 1919, but we are not likely to underestimate the dangers that threaten democracy today. And while we may differ in our diagnosis of the ills that threaten the life of the democratic states, there is one weakness in modern democracy that has been so obvious and so widespread that it has been taken as a necessary fault in the democratic system. Since modern democracies notably lacked forceful leaders, since the exaltation of the leader was the political mark of the systems that threaten the destruction of the democratic world, there was a temptation to make the best of a bad job and to emphasise the power of the community, the strength of spontaneous action, the dangers of hero-worship all to the end that the failure of the democratic systems in Europe to produce leaders or, if they were produced, to admit them to power, should be turned from being an ominous sign of weakness to a proof of moral and intellectual superiority. And this comforting heresy, this neglect of the role of the democratic chief as a maker of opinion as well as a servant of it, as a farseeing interpreter of the people's needs as well as the obedient instrument of its decisions, might have become orthodoxy all over the democratic world, had not the greatest of democratic states given itself, in time, as elected chief a man who in daring and energy rivalled the Dictators and yet who never forgot that he was a servant of the people, not a master. It is not too much to say that, as the numbed and frightened peoples of the free nations saw the clouds grow till they covered the whole sky and felt in their bones that, in the coming storm, no canal-boat navigators of the type with which Britain and France were alike afflicted were of any use, only the spectacle of the daring pilot whom the people of the United States had commissioned to steer them to safety kept alive faith in the choice of their rulers by the people. And in the great crisis of the war which has thrown Britain and the United States together in a common partnership of good and evil fortune, the successes and failures of democratic leadership as exemplified by Mr Roosevelt have their own special interest. Unless the nature of that leadership is understood we cannot plan for a future in which the terrible lessons of 1919-1939 can be learned—for the last time. The most patient teachers tire of totally unteachable pupils, and if we do not master the problem of democratic leadership at this attempt we shall not be given another chance.

WHEN HE COMPLETES his third term of office, Franklin Delano Roosevelt will have been President of the United States for a longer time than Napoleon I was Emperor of the French. Had he no other claim on our attention he would have that provided by his unprecedented triple election to one of the two greatest elective offices of the world. And no Pope of modern times has been so great a world figure or so much a breaker of precedent as President Roosevelt has been. Of course, it would be idle to pretend that the circumstances of the age, and the shift in power that has made the role of the United States of such overwhelming importance, have not had more to do with the great role played by Mr Roosevelt than have exclusively personal qualities. Because the United States is by far the most powerful industrial state, because its role as an embodiment of free principles and institutions is primary in the contemporary world, *any* President of the United States would be a figure of world importance in this crisis. His very weakness would be a factor in the defeat or victory of freedom. The office of President of the United States is too great for its holder not to be a force in world events. But he can be a positive or a negative force. And that Mr. Roosevelt has been a positive force is to be seen in a dozen aspects of the contemporary world.

The decision of the American people to elect Mr Roosevelt for a third term is proof of the acceptance by the American people of the reality of the modern world, its revolutionary character, its dreadful possibilities of disaster and of retreat from the hopes of human progress which have been held as a religious faith for over one hundred and fifty years. The American people has seen its way of life menaced as never before, its inheritance of free choice threatened with destruction by the appearance of a world in which the only way to survive in a system of great tyrannies would be to imitate them. But although Herr Hitler would sooner or later have given a lesson of inescapable force to the American people, he might, in America as in other countries, have been allowed to delay giving that lesson until its learning would have come too late. For upsetting this part of Herr Hitler's time-table the main credit must go to Mr. Roosevelt, and that this is appreciated by the Nazis the frenzied and hysterical abuse that they have long poured out on the President sufficiently proves.

There are many qualities present in the equipment of Mr Roosevelt that would mark him out in any society. Despite the infantile paralysis that crippled him over twenty years ago and which would have ended the active life of a less tenacious man, he gives an impression of great physical power. Being President of the United States is one of the most exhausting jobs in the world ; the President has to combine being a king with being a prime minister ; his lightest word may be of importance to thousands ; his every minute is doled out to this task or that. Yet Mr Roosevelt has thrived on a burden greater than any of his predecessors save Lincoln has known and he has borne that burden twice as long as Lincoln. Fatigue comes to him rarely and is quickly recovered from. Gravity he knows and shows in speech and manner, but none of that black melancholy which Lincoln knew, none of that impatience with the absurdity and baseness of the world which was a weakness of his great predecessor, Woodrow Wilson.

Since as a young man he performed his first electoral miracle in getting elected to the New York legislature, in 1910, from a rockbound Republican district as a Democrat, he has been a master of all the arts that win friends and allies, in single spies and in armies. No one who saw the fervent crowds of 1936 waiting to see their deliverer, shouting their love for the man who had not forgotten the 'forgotten' men—and women—of the United States need be told that Mr Roosevelt has the indefinable magic talent of a leader of masses or of mobs. Hitler has it too, so it is not a quality to be admired without due caution, but it is the authentic magic that Gladstone had, that in American history Clay and Douglas and Bryan had. And its absence in the European democratic leaders in the years between 1931 and 1939 was a disaster.

Mr Roosevelt is an orator and he was known to be an orator to the Democratic politicians who had heard him nominate Al Smith in 1924 in a speech that seemed, in its art and power, to come from another world than that in whose drab factories machine-made eulogies are turned out.[1] But Mr Roosevelt's oratorical talents would not have been the force in American and in world-history which they have been if it had not been for the invention of radio. It is not only that Mr Roosevelt's voice and oratorical technique are so admirably adapted to this medium that the listener has the feeling that it was specially invented for him. But he has made of this technical accomplishment one of the most effective instruments of government. His 'fireside chats' have been a means of restoring the direct relationship between the leader and the led that marked ancient democracy. American crowds in streets and clubs and bars as well as in homes have become accustomed to the idea of being appealed to for support ; but they have also become accustomed to being told what to support, to listening to a report on the state and needs of the nation which the President uses as a basis for stimulating action.

The direct appeal to the people on the air was one way of getting round the separation of the executive from the legislature in the American system. What was said to the nation was re-echoed in Congress ; it was often an appeal to the common sovereign of both President and Congress, 'We, the People of the United States.' Nor was this the only link between the people and the President developed if not invented by Mr Roosevelt. His distant cousin and uncle-in-law, Theodore Roosevelt, had made the presidential Press conferences a means of informing, influencing and, his enemies said, distorting public opinion. Other Presidents had imitated or tried to imitate him. But it was President Franklin D. Roosevelt who made of the Press conference

---

[1] What the public remembered of this first great Roosevelt speech was the description of Al Smith as 'the Happy Warrior.' This application of Wordsworth's phrase to so un-Wordsworthian a character was the happy thought not of Mr Roosevelt but of Justice Proskauer.

F

a kind of third house of Congress in which the President made announcements, answered or parried questions, like a Prime Minister on the front bench. To face and handle a hundred American newspapermen twice a week was a test of temper, of judgment and of ready wit that Mr Roosevelt passed brilliantly. And, lastly, Mr Roosevelt made of his addresses to Congress and his interviews with congressional leaders opportunities to display his talent for managing men, many of them political veterans and all of them men with their own sense of power and their own sense of direct political responsibility to their state or district.

If Mr Roosevelt had anything to say, he was admirably equipped to say it. If he had anything he wanted to do, he had the power of securing support for his projects. But the man who was overwhelmingly elected President in 1932 was not known to have anything to say that differed much from what others had said, and he had not given signs of special energy or courage in his actions. He had been a vigorous Assistant-Secretary of the Navy (the Navy had been his first love and had he had his own way he would have been a naval officer). But although his role in the last war was important, it was still subordinate. As Governor of New York he found himself, like all other state executives, faced with problems that only the Union could tackle and the Union under Mr Hoover had other ideas of the duty of the Federal government. Mr Roosevelt was made Democratic nominee in 1932 as a result of the alliance of the West and South against the East. And the allies chose him because he was Governor of New York, and so marked by all political precedent as the most 'available' of all possible candidates. He was 'wet'— and Protestant ; he was a New Yorker—and a farmer ; he had carried New York in 1928 and in 1932. And his manager, Mr Farley, had won to his support practical politicians in all parts of the Union. But it is safe to say that few who voted for Mr Roosevelt knew what they were getting, and millions who voted for him did so simply as the most effective protest against the policies or the bad luck of Mr Hoover. There were observers who thought, with resignation or despair, that the United States, at one of the greatest crises in its history, had chosen as President a good-looking orator who would seek to avoid action, who would be averse from risk and innovation, one who might well conduct the Union to destruction by gentlemanly obedience to the rules. Few noted the content of the candidate's speeches and fewer, if they saw the implications of those speeches, believed that the new President would act according to the lights he had made visible.

Less than two months before the first inauguration of Mr Roosevelt, Hitler became Chancellor, and what the world soon came to see as a contest began. For in both Germany and America the old order was breaking down and a crisis of faith was making reconstruction more difficult psychologically than materially. The world knows the Hitler remedy ; preparation for war, which 'cured' unemployment, and the creation of a barbaric religion that made war natural and, indeed, welcome to the really converted. The heretics and sceptics were silenced by terror. Mr Roosevelt restored faith by other means. He had learned in the years of his slow convalescence from his personal disaster what suffering was and what patience could and could not do. Mrs Roosevelt, whom the superficially sophisticated thought of as a handicap, was a link of the greatest value with the poor, the unfortunate and their friends and leaders. The 'New Deal' began with banks closed, with local government bankrupt or near it, with over ten million unemployed. The New Deal was less a programme than an attitude. Mr Roosevelt, far from being a cautious and timid clinger to precedent, was almost too confident an experimenter. That a thing had not been tried before was, if anything, a reason for trying it now. And the politician who had been thought not firm enough became known for his fighting obstinacy once he had 'his Dutch up.'

In his attacks on what had been the sacred rights and, still more sacred, the prestige of 'business,' Mr Roosevelt showed no timidity. In his conviction that he, better than any newspaper owner or old-style politician, knew what the people wanted or needed, there has been no faltering. He has continued to fight battles, like that against the old Supreme Court, when prudent advisers have longed for retreat, and he has snatched at least tactical victories out of apparently hopeless situations. But he has done this without ever forgetting that he is a leader in the democratic sense, that he is not a dictator whose rightness is axiomatic and whose whims have the force of law. Despite the wails of the timid, he has not endangered the fundamental democratic process, and the American people, even when it has refused to follow him, has shown its contempt for the spreaders of panic and the counsellors of despair.

Since his authority has been great and for brief moments uncontested, and since understanding of the working of American politics has been rare in Europe, he has been thought to have more untrammelled power than he has had. So he has been reproached for caution and indecision when, given the American situation, he was driving at a speed that was just short of reckless. From the moment when, in the first year of office, the 'honeymoon' of the New Deal was over, Mr Roosevelt has had in his own country and in his own party to take account of a powerful, resourceful and sometimes unscrupulous opposition. He has had to display every day that 'sense of possibilities' that Cavour thought the greatest gift of a statesman. And as a democratic politician, as leader of a free political party and chief executive of a free state, he has had to make compromises that naturally irritate the purist who has neither the temptations nor the duties of the statesman.

AT THE BASIS of Mr Roosevelt's power has been his acceptance and his utilisation of his role as the leader of a free party and the chief of a free government. He did not found the Democratic party ; he did not create the American constitution. He has taken both as he found them ; he has modified them but they have not been fundamentally altered. It is easier to state briefly his relation to the constitutional system than to the party system. Congress and the Supreme Court have their own independent duties and powers. Mr Roosevelt can influence Congress by speech, by popular pressure, by his own personality and by his role as a party leader. He can influence the Supreme Court by his appointments to it.[1] That he has done both, the immense changes he has wrought in the American governmental structure bear witness.

But it is in his relationship to the American party system that his acceptance of limitations and his ability to work within them are most evident. And only if those limitations are understood

---

[1] All members of the Supreme Court save one owe their present position to Mr Roosevelt Yet the Court is in many things as divided as ever. The United States is not a country where political unanimity can easily take root.

can the fashion in which Mr Roosevelt has made the United States a bastion of freedom be understood.

Mr Roosevelt is head of the Democratic party, and it has had no such leader since the days of its founder, the President's hero, General Andrew Jackson. But the Democratic party is an historical phenomenon like the Republican party. Most of its leaders are Democrats because their fathers were Democrats before them.[1] To be white in South Carolina, to be poor in New York was, in nearly every case, to be a Democrat as well. As the party that was usually in opposition, and which got power only when there was general discontent with the administration of the United States by Business, the Democrats were usually more 'liberal' than the Republicans, but many Democrats were much less liberal than many Republicans. In the great crisis of 1932 the Democrats were turned to, not because they were liberal, much less radical, but because they were out of office.

It was as head of this party that Mr Roosevelt was first elected. And he has remained head of that party. He has attempted to mould it more in his own image ; he has attempted (with very little success) to make loyalty to his programme a test of party orthodoxy ; but he has done nothing that would destroy it, or weaken its hold on any of the sections and regions that cling to it. He has not tried to make a wholly new and consistent party under the old or under a new name. To have done that would have been to risk losing his chance of immediate effective action. He might have succeeded, he might have failed, but the attempt would have taken time and energy that could not be spared from greater needs. And Mr Roosevelt's role, as a leader of America in the world crisis, can only be appreciated justly if it is remembered that he had to work within the historical framework of the American political system. That system for good historical and geographical reasons is not designed to make decisive action speedy or easy. Mr Roosevelt has had to make a machine over-provided with brakes move quickly enough to compete with machines which have no brakes at all. He has, by political virtuosity which few can appreciate, managed to do this.[2]

[1] This is true of the President himself. All the Roosevelts were Democrats except the Oyster Bay branch to which Theodore belonged.
[2] In 1938 Mr Roosevelt attempted to 'purge' certain Democratic Senators and one Representative. Except in the case of the Representative, he failed. Voters who had supported him in 1932 and 1936 were not prepared to vote against their local leaders even though those leaders

There were few supporters or enemies of Mr Roosevelt who were deceived as to the character of the Nazi revolution. There were inveterate anti-Semites and lay and clerical demagogues of whom Father Coughlin was the first in his bad eminence. There were German-Americans, mostly recent immigrants, who joined the 'Friends of the New Germany,' which became the 'Bund.' But there was little sign in America of that combination of sentimentality and gullibility which in England made the task of the Nazi confidence tricksters easy. Some men and women who, like Dr Buchman, lived in terror of Bolshevism, might thank God for Hitler ; big business leaders might think it easy to do business with Hitler or, at any rate, necessary ; profoundly ignorant innocents abroad like Mr Henry Ford might take Hitler medals. But on the whole the American public mind was never as muddled on the meaning of the Nazi revolution as was the English. The country that had had to put up with Al Capone for a while was able to recognise gangsters where English peers, publicists and parsons saw rather pathetic figures only needing kindness to be converted to prosperity and progress through peace. Nor were the Americans taken in by the façade of respectable German Christian gentlemen whom Hitler used as more or less unconscious tools. They knew that the worst American political machines had never gone short of respectable figure-heads to deceive the unwary. It was not necessary to convert the American people to the view that Nazism was bad ; it *was* necessary to convert them to the view that its badness concerned them, that its dangers were dangers for the United States as well as for Britain or France. And it was necessary to convert the American people to the view that they could and should do something to aid the powers who would have to withstand the blow when the acceptable time for German aggression came. The coalition that elected Mr Roosevelt in 1932 was, if possible, more divided on this point than on any other. It was a matter of basic radical orthodoxy that the United States had been betrayed, mainly by British propaganda, into entry to a quarrel that was no business

had been more or less open opponents of the leader of the party. Those who rejoiced in the failure of the purge were sometimes to be found with the critics who lamented that Mr Roosevelt did—and does—negotiate with and make concessions to 'bosses' like Mr Hague of Jersey City. If Mr Roosevelt could impose a unified policy on his party and induce voters over the Union to punish disobedience to it, he might be able to afford to quarrel with the Hagues of this world. As it is he cannot afford to be on the side of the angels all the time and everywhere.

of the American people. Not only had American intervention, by giving complete victory to the Allies, made possible the infamous Treaty of Versailles, the fount of all our woes, but during the war the liberal gains of the first Wilson administration had been thrown away. To the war was attributed not only death and famine in Europe but intervention against the Russian Revolution, the anti-radical panic whose most famous victims were Sacco and Vanzetti, the control of the United States by the interests which elected Harding and Coolidge and the orgy of speculative lending to Europe which brought about the crash of 1929. To believe all this, to be bitterly anti-militarist, to believe that 'force settles nothing,' that wars were simply devices of the armament companies or ways of killing competition, these were the credentials of radical orthodoxy. In some areas this orthodox doctrine had its living confessors, like Senator George Norris of Nebraska, or had the memory of its martyrs kept green, of men like Representative Lindbergh of Minnesota who had fought war and the bankers and Rome, or like the late Senator La Follette of Wisconsin whose name was a passport to political power over a great part of the west and whose ally, Senator Wheeler of Montana, was the trusted leader of the western radical elements in the Democratic party.

Nor was it only among the regular politicians that ceremonial washing of the hands of the guilt of Wilsonism was customary. Divines like Dr Charles Clayton Morrison still hoped to abolish war by pious resolution, by leading the nations to the mourner's bench, and pacificism tended to replace belief in Prohibition as a test of Protestant orthodoxy.

It was only in the South that the implications of the rise of Nazi Germany were understood. In the South, it was useless to assert that wars settled nothing ; having been on the losing side in one of the greatest of modern wars, the Southerners knew better. To them the risks of merely killing Hitler with your mouth, of ignoring what *he* might choose to do, were evident. And in the South the simple tradition that the soldier and sailor was a hero, not a licensed murderer or a fool, was still lively. But in the South was also concentrated the most effective resistance within Mr Roosevelt's own party to his social policy. Senator Carter Glass of Virginia would allow no attack on the memory of Woodrow Wilson to pass unrebuked and no illustration of the illusion that Hitlerism could be killed by kindness or by pious opinions to pass unexposed, but he likewise allowed few opportunities of attacking the economic policy of the New Deal to pass either. The South understood Mr Roosevelt's interest in the Navy but, in its political ruling class at least, disliked his friendly interest in trade unions. Each move of the President to increase the power of the United States on air, land or sea was approved by those elements in his party with whom he was least in sympathy on other grounds and, at best, tolerated by the politicians and publicists who most warmly approved of the President's domestic policy.

It was not only inside his own party that the President had to watch for strains. The Republicans, chastened by their ignominious defeat on the home front, were looking for an issue. What could be better than the hoisting of the flag under which they had been enabled to elect a Harding ? So although some leading Republicans like Senator Austin and Representative Wadsworth were as alive as the President himself to the Hitler danger, the minority party was more and more tempted to cater to the large body of Americans who were determined not to enter the war of 1917.

This was the policy embodied in the various Neutrality acts that were enacted from 1935 to 1939. It was assumed as self-evident truth that the United States had entered the last war because of the selfish interests of bankers who had lent money to the British. Both the bankers and the British had an interest in bringing the United States into the war, and they had befuddled the American mind with propaganda about German atrocities and the rights of American citizens on the high seas and democracy and liberty. So a stout refusal to listen to any arguments or appeals that might involve action, or that implied any danger to the United States, became the sign of critical intelligence. Arguments were not answered, they were merely labelled 'propaganda.' Nations which had defaulted on their war debts were barred from the American money market ; American ships were forbidden to sail in war zones ; Americans were, except in a few special cases, forbidden to sail on belligerent ships. The munitions trade was regarded as the main cause of American involvement in the war of 1914-1918, so all export of arms was forbidden in war-time. As far as the dread of a repetition of American intervention in 1917 was a brake on Hitler's conditioning of the German people for war, this neutrality legislation reassured both the Führer and his people. They had nothing to fear from the United States as long as the American people believed that world war could be prevented by pious resolution or, if that failed, that its impact on the United States could be reduced by legislation to mere economic inconvenience.[1] Mr Roosevelt has since admitted that his acceptance of this Neutrality legislation was a mistake. It may be guessed that he did not share the cheerful illusions of its sponsors, but in his first term of office it was still possible to believe that the storm would blow over, that the western powers would combine while there was yet time to keep Hitler's Germany impotent. Was it worth while, then, to provoke in America a violent storm by revealing open scepticism about the efficacy of legislating peace and security ? Such a stand would alienate just those elements of the Roosevelt coalition whose loyal support was most necessary for the extension and defence of the President's domestic programme. A split on this issue would throw the President into the arms of the reactionary Southern section of his own party, and give the Republicans their best chance of over-throwing the New Deal under the guise of saving American boys from European battlefields. And there was abundant evidence that American public opinion was far from being prepared to take any active steps or run any risks to stabilise the world situation. Certainty that the power of the United States could be relied on to resist a German attack on the hesitating democracies, or even that benevolent neutrality could be relied on, would have stiffened the backs of many a European ruler. But when the American gunboat *Panay* was attacked on the Yangtse in 1937 by Japanese planes the reaction of many Americans was to ask why an American gunboat was there at all. And more striking was the retreat forced on the President by the reception of the speech he made in Chicago in 1937. There he spoke of a 'quarantine' to be imposed by the free peoples on the aggressors. But the American people

[1] The most remarkable example of this national superstition, that enacted law is practically omnipotent, was the so-called 'Ludlow' amendment which proposed to make it impossible for the United States to declare war without a national plebiscite. It took a good deal of pressure from the Administration to defeat this measure in Congress. Had it been adopted as a constitutional amendment it would not have had any practical effect since, in the event, Germany declared war on the United States, but it would have had a profound psychological effect in Europe, making resistance to Hitler far more of a strain on the faith of the free peoples that, in time, the American people would realise that their survival, as *a free people*, was bound up with the freedom of Europe and Asia.

had learned from Abyssinia that effective resistance to the aggressor cannot be limited in scope, and the President's seed fell on very barren ground. Europe was disillusioned, and the only good result was that the American man in the street had brought home to him the truth that, when and if he did come to support active measures, he was, however he might hate to admit the fact, accepting a liability whose extent not he but the aggressors would determine. He had to 'put up or shut up.' He was not yet ready to put up so the President had to shut up.

Yet the change in the internal and external situation was having its effect. By the time Mr Roosevelt had been overwhelmingly re-elected, the European situation had got worse. With the military occupation of the Rhineland by the Nazis the military situation in Europe had been transformed. Britain and France, by themselves, had no longer the power to intimidate Germany into good external behaviour. The collapse of sanctions deprived the League of Nations of authority and sent the small countries scurrying to cover. And the Spanish Civil War was seen in America in its true light, as the first act in a new European war. But by following British policy, and denying the legal Spanish government its right to buy arms in the American market, Mr Roosevelt played into the hands of the Isolationists. For the existing law did not cover civil wars ; it was necessary first of all by administrative pressure and then by a new statute to take from the Spanish Republican government the right to buy arms. The Isolationists at first rejoiced, but carried away by their sympathy for the Spanish Republic, and obsessed with the view that there was only one risk of war, aid to Britain and France, some of their leaders, like Senator Nye, strongly supported selling arms to Spain. But it was a worthless debating point to underline the inconsistency. The Administration's Spanish policy greatly weakened its position when it attempted to secure a repeal or amendment of the Neutrality legislation. Munich further weakened the President's position. With generous, if uncritical, indignation the American people added the betrayal of Czechoslovakia to the betrayal of China and Spain, not a little helped by the rash language of some defenders of Mr Chamberlain's policy who seemed to be looking forward to a series of further 'settlements' of this type. So there combined against Mr Roosevelt's proposal to amend the Neutrality laws to permit the sale of arms in war-time the pro-Germans, the indifferentists, the pacifists and the radical elements who were either persuaded that the world cause of democracy was no business of the United States, or that the France of Daladier and the England of Chamberlain were unsatisfactory champions of it. From Mr Hamilton Fish, who thought there was a good deal to be said for the German case, to Senator Borah, who in his sublime complacency was convinced on the strength of his private intelligence service that there would be no war, most Republicans combined with enough Democrats to prevent any alteration of the law. When Congress met again war had broken out, and the formidable character of German power and the success of German diplomacy were illustrated by the conquest of Poland and the neutralisation of Russia.

To secure the amendment of the Neutrality laws to allow Britain and France to draw on American manufacturing resources was no easy matter. The fact that war had come was enough to awaken the most lively terrors of a people conditioned to regard war as evil, absurd—and avoidable. The passivity of France and Britain after the annihilation of Poland made it easy to accept the thesis that this was a 'phoney' war. The change in the Communist line which followed the Ribbentrop-Molotov pact meant that many organisations under Communist control suddenly reversed themselves and began to spread a view of the war and of the proper American attitude to the war indistinguishable from that encouraged by the Nazi propaganda machine. And these Communist-controlled societies and unions had among their members many thousands of loyal, active, if not very perspicacious, New Dealers. Yet Mr Roosevelt succeeded ; at the price of further concessions limiting the free action of American citizens, he secured that Britain and France could buy armaments, that is, aeroplanes, in the United States. They had to pay cash for them and remove them in their own ships. This policy of 'cash and carry' was recommended to the American people as a way of keeping them out of war. For it made more certain what was then taken as axiomatic, that the western powers with their much greater resources would win, and win especially easily if the Germans were forced into the suicidal folly of an offensive, for had not the experts proved that offensives were inevitably disastrous to the attackers ? The illusions of the American people may not have been wholly shared by the President, but they were shared by the British people and, apparently, by its rulers. With American industry to draw on, the odds on Allied victory, to be won cheaply if not quickly, were overwhelming. It was in this frame of mind that the American people reproved the tepidness of Allied support for Finland. Britain and France were in no danger of defeat and could afford to go crusading against Russia as well as against Germany. War was still a matter of pure principle, not a desperate struggle for survival. Indeed, it was the soundness of the American heart that accounted for some of the confusion in the American head. Whereas Wilson in 1914 had asked for emotional as well as legal neutrality, Mr Roosevelt asked for no suspension of moral judgment. And the American people, condemning German aggression and tyranny, expected from the active agents of German chastisement chemically clean hands and a most pedantic regard for international law, an attitude which would have struck them as highly unrealistic if the question at issue had been the methods of a crusading District Attorney like young Mr Dewey of New York.

SUCH WAS THE AMERICA in which Mr Roosevelt had to work in the months of the 'phoney' war. And it is not a matter for surprise that American reaction to the realities revealed by the conquest of Norway, Holland, Belgium, France was a little slower than that of the President. What was surprising was that the American people followed the President so quickly. He reaped his reward for his understanding of the human and natural reluctance of the people to face the whole terrible truth, that the world (including the United States) was now in danger of conquest or forced conformity to the new barbarism. But the American people reacted far more quickly than those normally well-informed observers, the practising politicians, had expected. Mr Wendell Willkie (who had no political experience or position) was imposed on the Republican party as their candidate because its normal leaders were so tied by the old commitments to various shades of now irrelevant Isolationism that to have put them up against the President would have been to invite a débâcle worse than that of 1936. And opposition to the President's unprecedented decision to run for a third term evaporated.

And the United States was saved the ordeal of a Presidential election fought on foreign policy where every campaign conflict could be exacerbated by skilful German action inside the United States. And, still more important, the conquered peoples of Europe and the British people in their finest and most dreadful hour were not left open to the temptation to make what terms they could with the Nazis under the threat that the next President of the United States might come into office pledged in effect, if not in form, to washing his hands of Europe.

All pretence of formal neutrality was abandoned when the Italian intervention was described as a 'stab in the back,' and desperate and unavailing efforts were made to keep France in the war. But only an American declaration of war could have done that, and the American people was not ready for a step that (it believed) was either desperate or superfluous.

But where Mr Roosevelt's hands were free he acted with decision and daring. He sold to Britain arms from the American reserves, defying both the opposition of the constitutional purists who asserted this to be (as it was) a highly unneutral act carried out without Congressional assent, and the fears of the timid who were certain that Britain was doomed and that these weapons would simply go to increase the spoils of war with which Germany would attack the United States. The same arguments and the same fears were insufficient to deter the President from transferring fifty American destroyers to Britain in exchange for bases in the West Indies, an act whose formally unneutral character made British conduct in the *Alabama* case look like pedantic legalism ! And when Mr Roosevelt was re-elected for the third time the whole world saw in his re-election the decision of the American people to prevent a German victory, *if possible* by non-belligerent means. The words of the President were now of world-wide import. The listeners to his 'fireside' chats were no longer merely the American citizens to whom the messages were formally addressed, but the whole world. The Nazi rulers of Europe, whose chief political weapon was the inculcation of despair, and the rulers of Britain whose chief political weapon was the sustenance of hope, both saw in the speeches of the President one of the most deadly weapons of the war. And as a spokesman of the hopes of the common man Mr Roosevelt had qualifications that were his and his alone. The fame of the New Deal, the knowledge of the kind of friends and enemies he had made, were now of the greatest value in propaganda. The German campaign against the 'pluto-democracies' might have had some success if it had not had to be directed against one whose record was that of hostility to the money power, to merely exploitative capitalism. No other American could, by his mere name and record, have made the task of Goebbels and Laval and Mussert and Déat so difficult. It was his record as a bold not to say reckless reformer, as the very antithesis of the drab, passive and unenterprising politicians in whose hands democracy in Europe had been weakened until the Nazis seemed merely to be giving the *coup de grâce*, that stood him in good stead now. The New Deal, as a symbol if not as a concrete programme, was the barrier to the sale of the New Order to the hungry, half-despairing, wholly bewildered peoples of Europe.

ONCE RE-ELECTED, Mr Roosevelt could devote time and thought how best to aid Britain and Greece (then the sole resisting powers in Europe) to carry on their fight against the Axis. And he invented the brilliant solution of 'lend-lease'. The American public was still irritated by the memory of the war debts. Britain could not borrow money nor was it certain that if she borrowed she could repay. So she was allowed to borrow goods, planes and ships and tanks—and if the United States later wanted to have them repaid, it was goods, planes, ships and tanks, that would be repaid. To keep Britain at war was to defend the United States.

But the United States was much better able to defend herself than she had been. Before 1939 the navy had been greatly developed under Mr Roosevelt, but the army was small and ill-equipped when war came in 1939. The adoption of conscription in 1940, in time of peace, if of danger, was the work of Congress although of a Congress led from the White House. By making two eminent Republicans, Messrs Stimson and Knox, Secretaries of War and the Navy, Mr Roosevelt, without dividing his own unique responsibility, recognised the national character of the defence effort. By calling on the great production engineer,

Mr Knudsen, of General Motors, to direct armament production, the positive skill of Big Business was called into service. All of these measures were denounced as inadequate by some and as war-mongering by others, the critics on the last score ranging from the open friends of Germany to the self-described spokesmen of Russia. But the American people was conscious of its danger and when, after the disasters of Greece and Libya, Hitler turned on Russia, there was far less reluctance to see the common interest of the U.S.A. and U.S.S.R. than many had feared. It is true that a minority which was almost a majority of the House of Representatives threatened to disrupt the new conscript army. But Congress was out of touch with a public feeling that wanted more energy, not less. If there was disappointment at the terms of the Atlantic Charter, it was a natural reflection of an ambiguous state of affairs. The United States was now hardly neutral. She had her first casualties when American destroyers were attacked by German submarines. So unnatural a situation could not last. If it was the decision to make no concessions to Japan that produced the final crisis, it merely precipitated it. The revolutionary character of the war was now evident to all but the wilfully blind. The veteran of the Senate Radicals, Mr Norris, who had voted against war in 1917, had long since refused to be bound by an irrelevant precedent. Pearl Harbor ensured that the minority of the American people which had clung to its hopes of immunity could rally to the defence of its country with no sense of resentment—except in the most irreconcilable and fanatical groups. Never was the United States more united and never had the United States been better prepared, materially and psychologically, on entry to a war. That is Mr Roosevelt's achievement. And he achieved this end by being a leader, not a mere mouthpiece of popular sentiment on one side or a dictator on the other. He has taken care that no harm befall the Commonwealth, and that has involved patience, resilience and a conviction that democratic unity, when it is at last formed, is worth its price in slowness in action and apparent hesitation in policy. And when it is necessary to note, and sometimes to regret, the concessions Mr Roosevelt has had to make to ill-informed American sentiment, concessions that have limited the effectiveness of his actions, it must at the same time never be forgotten that only by this constant regard for the strength and weakness of his own people could he have become and have remained the educator and leader of the American nation. And on that leadership there has more than once depended the hope of freedom in the world.

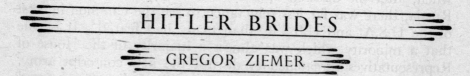

HITLER BRIDES

GREGOR ZIEMER

'Girls,' said the teacher, 'you are old enough to know. Our Fuehrer wants and needs soldiers, to destroy his enemies. His enemies hate us ; but we not only hate—we will eliminate them. You all know that soldiers don't just grow by themselves. They must be born. Don't wait too long. You are now fifteen. A year or two, and you can have your babies. Meanwhile, become acquainted with some good Aryan soldier.'

I was in a classroom of the *Mittelschule fuer Maedchen* (intermediate school for girls) in Luckenwalde, fifty miles from Berlin, having come with a pass from the Nazi Minister of Education, Dr. Bernhard Rust. The twenty girls who packed the dingy classroom were fascinated. Their eyes were fixed in a glassy stare on the speaker. The teacher was a woman past middle age. She wore a dark-blue skirt, a stiff white blouse. Her grey hair was combed back in tight strands. Over her sunken chest she had pinned a swastika button with the letters RLD, indicating that she was a member of the *Reichs Lehrer Bund* (the Nazi teacher's league), a Hitler disciple.

The teacher continued : 'I was, alas, brought up in a régime that did not have the courage to let us disregard restrictive social bonds. But our Fuehrer has ended all these conventions. He has created a new conception of society. Girls, remember your mission. You must have children and have them as soon as you can.'

It can be assumed that most of those girls are mothers by now. Bearing children for Hitler was made most attractive and important for them in that school, as in all Nazi schools where idolatry of Hitler is the basis of the teaching. All German children are strictly controlled by the Nazi School Ministry. This control begins before the child is born, reaches into the home and gradually tightens, until not a single minute belongs to the child or his parents. The German child goes to school to learn not facts but Nazi doctrine. Classroom work can at any time be superseded by Nazi Party activities. The boy at six becomes a *Pimpf* (little fellow). He wears a uniform—brown shorts, shirt and trench cap. Each boy has a *Leistungbuch*, a permanent record in which are noted all his achievements. He learns to march, shoot, drill, to act and think like a soldier. At ten he is promoted to the *Jungvolk* (Young Folk). His uniform is more military. The party demands more of him. 'We teach boys enough to make obedient soldiers,' a Nazi teacher told me. The Hitler Youth—HJ—in which boys serve from fourteen to eighteen is the next step. The HJ emphasises the characteristics of full-fledged soldiers. During this period the schools stress Hitlerized history, geography and ideology, military geometry, science and a foreign language. Since the war the HJ has become a secondary army, with all the toughness, cruelty and sadistic intensity one might expect it to have.

The girls have similar organisations. All schoolgirls under fourteen are *Jungmaedel* (Young Girls). From fourteen to eighteen they are BDM's (League of German Girls). In all grades girls are taught less than the boys, with emphasis on training for motherhood. BDM girls are fully instructed in conception, childbirth and homekeeping. They are frequently urged by teachers to become Hitler Brides and have state babies. And they do.

Perhaps never before in history has any political machine been as diabolically clever in its ruthless exploitation of youth as the Nazi machine. The Nazis have used every chicanery to soften the minds and morals of German girls until they are nothing but first-class breeders unhampered by ties of marriage or home. What effect the kind of teaching I saw has on young girls I realised clearly in my visits to special homes maintained all over Germany for pregnant, unmarried girls—Hitler Brides.

There is a typical home for Hitler Brides at Altenau, a small city not far from Berlin. It is on the outskirts of the town, in a heavy growth of Harz pines. I climbed a winding path and then some stone steps to a spacious porch running half-way

G

around the house. It was ten in the morning on a cool, sunny spring day in May. The house mother, a tall, lean woman in her fifties, greeted me and led me to the side of the house where a row of young girls, many in advanced stages of pregnancy, were lying in deck chairs sunning themselves. They looked feminine enough, but never have I seen more fanaticism, mingled with hatred, than in some of those girls. In one particularly. She was small, with short, tousled blonde hair. Her features worked under the strain of emotional fanaticism.

'If you have come to see Hitler Brides,' she said, 'you are seeing them. And we're proud to be Hitler Brides, aren't we ?'

'Yes !' the others agreed vehemently.

'What nationality are you ?' the blonde asked. I said I was an American. A dead silence followed.

'Just wait,' the girl said. 'We will have children—boys. They will grow into men—men who will be glad to die for the Fuehrer, our Saviour. Then our enemies—and that means you Americans as well—can run for your lives.'

This education of girls for breeding soldiers is only one phase of Hitler's education programme. The other, conditioning boys for death on the battlefield, goes on with increased fury. How Nazi teachers go about indoctrinating boys with this desire to give up their lives for Hitler I observed in the small town of Rheinsberg, about sixty miles north-west of Berlin. The teacher had a map of the world with circles drawn around various spots. Since many German teachers used that device, I gather the idea came from Berlin. The circles marked these countries as happy hunting-grounds for young Nazis : South America, part of Africa, Poland, Yugoslavia, England, Russia, the United States. This teacher, as did so many others, first used the psychological lever of fear ; then he roused the superiority complex of the young Prussians. He declared that the encircled countries were waiting to pounce on Germany, but fate did not will that these inferior nations should rule over Germany. German culture and German strength would prevail, he told them. These threats of conquest— and promises of victory—led to the grand conclusion of all this teaching : There was only one great man in the world, Adolf Hitler. This man would make them strong. But in return they had to promise they would do everything Adolf Hitler asked of them. They would have to think of him always. They must think of him as a man who could do what nobody else could do—make Germany the leader of the whole world. And then someday all Germans would be leaders. But there was one thing—and he repeated it—they must all be ready to die for Hitler, die if need be fighting.

Those boys' eyes were wide with conviction. And when at the end of the class the teacher ordered them to 'Heil Hitler,' they did it as if they knew they would be condemned to everlasting damnation if they hesitated. But at the same time there was an arrogance on their faces. I encountered arrogance often : once on one of the picturesque Rhine boats crawling past famous old castles. A group of Hitler boys informed me that the United States had nothing that could compare with the beauties of the Rhine.

I tried to explain about our Rockies, the Mississippi, the Hudson, the Columbia. They answered : 'Well, if that's true and if you have all those things, we'll see for ourselves.'

'When ?' I asked.

'Our Fuehrer has told us that before we are grown up we will be in possession of America.'

I wanted to know when Hitler had said that.

'He has told our teachers, and our teachers have told us,' was the answer.

Just then we were joined by a man in civilian clothes. He was a teacher on holiday. Promptly he launched into a violent lecture. He was convinced that Hitler would sweep the world simply because he knew how to grip young people, how to make them feel powerful, to create in them a desire to conquer and rule. Never before, he argued, had any leader ever given his youth what Hitler was giving them—a determination to assert themselves, to look upon the world as a place to fight and conquer. He was almost in hysterics before he was through.

It was the same everywhere. In the universities, in the youth organizations, in the labour camps. Hitler is indeed conditioning a whole generation to obedience, to sacrifice, to a desire to fight, to win, to die if necessary. That many expect to die for Hitler is most obvious at those promotion ceremonies when Hitler *Pimpfs* become *Jungvolk* or when *Jungvolk* become Hitler Youth or when *Jungmaedel* become members of the *Bund Deutscher Maedel*.

One initiation rite I remember took place near the hospital

where Hitler recuperated after the last war—the place where on November 11, 1918, he paced the floor all night and swore eternal vengeance against the world. It is outside the walls of Pasewalk, an old city in northern Germany. There on an open field, a hundred selected *Jungmaedel* had gathered on the night before Hitler's birthday. The girls sat around a big bonfire waiting. That day they had stood reverently in the room where Hitler says his wrath had forced him to leave his sick bed and become the saviour of Germany. All day their souls had been given preliminary emotional rations to condition them for the climax.

Around the fire they sang—the Horst Wessel song and others. One I recall especially. It can be found on page 82 of the official Hitler song-book for girls.

> Many must die and sink into the grave
> Before our goal is reached and our banners in victory wave.
> You who are left behind are branded with the sign of death.
> You will have to learn
> That happiness and bliss only you can earn
> Who bleed and die
> And leave your life behind.
> For our Lord so strong and mighty,
> For our Saviour, Adolf Hitler,
> Sieg Heil, Sieg Heil !

'German boys and girls are in deadly earnest,' Dr. Rust shouted at me in Berlin.

Yes, Dr. Rust. Yes, Herr Hitler. We heard you. You have challenged us. We accept the challenge. Our youth have been educated for life ; yours, for death. In the final test, life will prevail.

THE DEATH OF DECENCY
WILLIAM L. SHIRER

In all the history of the human race there is no record of a highly cultured nation being so systematically and completely poisoned by the suppression of truth as Hitler's Third Reich. The Germany of Science and Truth is dead. The soul of a great and talented people has died, and with it most of the conceptions of morality and ethics and decency which had been built up with so much labour in the western world.

The effect, when you saw it in daily life in Germany, took your breath away. I can show what I mean by an example. There was a German general who, everyone knew, was half Jewish. Hitler badly wanted the man in the army, but he wouldn't have any Jews. Nazi pressure was brought to bear on the general's Aryan mother. A 'trial' was arranged. And this mother, a respectable woman, did something she wouldn't have dreamed of doing ten years before. She swore that her Jewish husband had not been the father of her child. She told the court she had had a lover. The lover was Aryan. He was the father of her child, she said. The general was 'proved' an Aryan.

Truth and the old concepts of honour and decency based on truth have lost their meaning, you see, in Hitler's Germany. The story of how this came about goes back just two decades.

Hitler's first great lie was his fake version of the 1918 defeat. He succeeded in convincing the overwhelming majority of the German people that Germany was beaten not on the battlefields but on the home front by 'defeatists, traitors, cowards, Jews and Marxists.' In nearly all his 1500 speeches he has driven this falsehood home, repeating it so often and with such force that most Germans believe it.

Hitler got permanently into power with a big lie. By blaming the fire which destroyed the Reichstag on the Communists—though the Nazis themselves were the real instigators—he was able not only to suppress a large political party but to frighten the people into electing a parliament which voted away its power to him.

More lies—and always big ones—paved the road down which Hitler, after 1934, brought Germany to war. By 1939 the drugging of the German people's sense of truth had become complete. From then on, Hitler and his henchmen could tell them anything that served their purposes and get by with it, no matter how great the lie.

An elderly, cultured German acquaintance brought home the frightening realisation of this to me during the first winter of the war. He had been an able man of science and, unlike most Germans, had travelled a great deal. Under the Republic he had been an ardent democrat and a good *European*. He liked the Italians, the French, the English, admired their cultures and was tolerant of their ways.

I do not remember when the great change came over him, but by the time the war came he was a different man. All the scepticism which his long training in science had given him and all the tolerance acquired by travel had disappeared. He swallowed Hitler's falsehoods completely. 'Der Fuehrer said this . . . Der Fuehrer said that . . .' he would shout, as if that alone disposed of all questions. We never got beyond what the Fuehrer said. The shabbiest fabrication of Hitler was a holy truth which it was blasphemous to doubt. What happened to him was symbolical of what happened to the German people.

No wonder that they swallowed the most absurd propaganda swindle of the war—the Munich beer-cellar bombing on the night of November 8, 1939, exactly twelve minutes after Hitler and *all* the big Party leaders had left it. Himmler and the Nazi press and radio screamed that the British secret service was responsible for the deed. This 'attempted assassination' of Hitler undoubtedly did stir up hatred of England. That was what Himmler wanted. That is why Himmler—in the opinion of most people in Berlin in a position to know—did the bombing himself. But to this day not more than a handful of Germans know it. It was another Reichstag fire.

Each new extension of the war called for a big lie to justify the aggression. On April 9, 1940, Foreign Minister Ribbentrop explained to the German people that Nazi forces had occupied Norway and Denmark 'to protect their freedom and independence against dark British designs.' You might have thought that even the Germans would have sniggered at that one. Nothing of the kind. My cultured old German scientist friend almost threw me out of his house for smiling myself at such a patent piece of hokum.

For the big lie to justify his completely unjustified attack on Holland and Belgium on May 10, 1940, Hitler forced his generals to concoct one of the silliest falsifications of the war. They drew up a 'document' claiming they had 'absolute proof' that the Allies were about to march through Holland and Belgium in an effort to seize the German Ruhr. Again, most Germans believed this childish lie.

It was the same on June 22, 1941, when Hitler turned on

Russia. He told the German people that the Red Army was about to attack him, that he had the proof and that he in his innocence —until a short time before, when the certainty of the attack dawned on him—had not even sent any tanks to the Russian border. And yet any resident of Berlin could have seen, as I did, hundreds of flat cars laden with tanks moving toward what the Nazis called 'the Russian front'—as early as July, 1940.

There is nothing haphazard about the suppression of truth in Germany. It is efficiently organised. Hitler himself lays down the main line. Goebbels merely ornaments Hitler's lies and sees that they are diffused.

Their diffusion is a work of art. Hitler often first enunciates a big lie in a speech. Goebbels and Himmler see to it that every last German in the Reich listens. Loud-speakers are set up in 10,000 village and town squares to carry the Leader's words. Schools, restaurants, theatres, factories, movies and stores are also forced to broadcast and rebroadcast them. All newspapers are forced to carry the complete text, the salient parts in black type. Editors are told how to write editorials emphasising Hitler's points. Thousands of feet of newsreels are made of Hitler delivering the speech.

But Hitler's speeches, important as they are, are not all. The Ministry of Education, under a Nazi fanatic, Bernhard Rust, sees to it that all the big lies are repeated incessantly to the school children in their daily lessons. Rust insists also that professors dwell on the 'Hitler truths' in their lectures in the universities. Millions of boys and girls in the Hitler youth organisations have the same falsehoods drummed into them at their meetings.

Special propagandists carry the Fuehrer's message to troops in the field and workers in the factories. And day in and day out the government-owned radio bombards countless millions with one falsehood after another. On May 9, 1940, the day before the German hordes thundered into Belgium and Holland, I wrote in my diary : 'What happens to the soul of a people who are fed such lies daily ?' I was too busy with the war to give the answer then. But I know now : Their soul rots away.

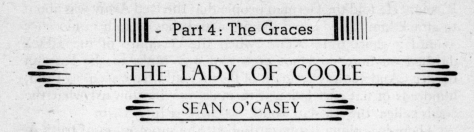
I had seen Lady Gregory sometime before, when I had been called to come to see her about an Abbey Theatre's first production of a play of mine, I had set out, clattering proudly through the paved Dublin streets; had passed through the richer entrance of the theatre for the first time; up the narrow staircase, and into the secretary's office. A long thin man had risen darkly before me in the dim light, waving a thin hand towards the far end of the narrow room, murmuring, this is Lady Gregory.

Slowly she rose from an office chair and came forward, her eyes gleaming, hand outstretched, a deep smile on her firm, rugged, and rather brownish face. Dressed in black she was, a simple brooch under her throat, a touch of something white under a long black silk veil that covered her grey hair, flowing gracefully behind, half-way down her back—an old elegant nun of a new order, a blend of the Lord Jesus Christ and of Puck, an order that Ireland had never known before, and wasn't likely to know again for a long time to come.

The pair of us got on grand together. We had many things in common besides the theatre. I loved pictures, and she was brimful of what her nephew, Hugh Lane, had done to diamond-clothe the walls of precious buildings with fair paintings by men of the day, and those done by their fathers in the old time before them. She loved fine books, and I was even a little ahead of her there. She saw humour sparkle from dead things; so did I, and we laughed serenely over tea in a hotel, looking out at Stephen's Green, I trying to look at home in the posh place, she eating bun after bun, and saying that our talk was all lovely; and, best of all, a play of mine, forcing queues to stand outside her little theatre, rang a chime of cheeriness over all our chat. So here I was, sober and thoughtful, reading a warm invitation to come and spend a week or two with her in Coole Park, in

County Galway, eager to go, but a little nervous at setting out to visit foreign parts.

After having freshly oiled my thick-leathered boots and tidied my hair cunningly ; having stuffed a stock of two pairs of clean socks, some handkerchiefs, and a couple of clean shirts into a fibre suitcase, here I was in the Galway Mail, of a morning early, on my way to Coole ; more than a little uneasy at the stormy thought of having to eat, drink, and sleep in a grand, great, big house, and talk to entertain its lady. When I broke my journey at the Ford of a King, to take a local train to Gort, there she was, waiting to guide me down—a stout, trim, black, little figure, standing still, grimly patient in the midst of the talkative, quick-moving crowd on the platform. A strange lone figure she looked in a third class carriage, stuck tight in a mass of peasants and small farmers, and they with baskets on their laps, live fowls, clucking for all they were worth, clutched in their hands, and one woman, young and lively, with a big goose, tied round leg and wing, so that it could only gabble, at her feet, mixing its comic cries with the eager animated chatter of the crowd.

—Dere, she said, suddenly pointing out of a window, dere's Craughwell where the police are half afraid to stir, eating and drinking and sleeping behind iron doors, thick stone walls, and steel-shuttered windows so that they can trust deir rifles out and fire without fear. We'll pass Ardrahan later on, and remember what Davis wrote :

> And, fleet as deer, the Normans ran,
> Through Curlews Pass and Ardrahan.

—An' will again, please God, an' will again, murmured a deep voice from a corner.

—She has a bit of a lisp, I thought, and it's a wonder I'm only after noticing it now. Look at her there, with all her elegance, well at ease among the chattering crowd of common people, so why shouldn't I be steady in my mind at coming to a big house, among rare silver and the best of china, sleeping in a bounteous bed, and handling divers tools at food, never seen before ? And I took heart and felt strong looking at the calm, handsome, old face smiling at the chatter and the cries of the frightened fowl. In the main, silent we had to sit, for she was at one end and I at another, so I sorted out my tumbling thoughts, watching her, and wondering by what devious ways she of the grandees had come so close to the poor plain people. It's little she's said herself of her younger days, dropping a bare hint here and there of how she thought and what she did then, in between Roxborough House where she was born and Coole Park, a few miles away, where she lived when she married ; and Tullyra Castle, another mile or two off, where Edward Martyn, spouse of terror, lived, told his beads, keeping his ears forever open for the warning cough of a clergyman.

Lady Gregory was the youngest child of a large family, and held a small corner in the activities surrounding the clever Elizabeth, the musical Gertrude, and the beautiful Adelaide, afterwards the mother of Sir Hugh Lane. I pictured her dissolving her own life into the life around her—as we all do—but preserving to herself a secret seed of thought that was to grow into a fine and steady understanding of literature ; into a shrewd and germinant companionship with Yeats ; into a wise and firm Dame Halberdier of the Irish Renaissance ; into a lively prop that kept the Irish Theatre standing ; into the humorous dramatic writer whose plays will do their devoirs freshly on many a stage, here and elsewhere, for many a year to come. It is most likely that she played games, went to church twice on Sundays, committed to memory innumerable woeful and winning texts of the Bible, looked over photos of trimly-dressed relatives and friends set down safe in the thick and gilded pages of an album ; some sitting on marble or brocaded chairs, others standing beside Doric pillars, with the whole world behind them, the women floating upward out of balloon-like dresses, beset with a forest of flounces, the men denoting manliness in bushy beard and whiskers. I saw her, at the end of the day, saying her prayers, before she climbed up a ladder on to a heavily-curtained bed to conjure sleep out of stuffy and most respectable air. Perhaps, some night or other, she chucked aside the tremendous curtains to have a look out of the window, wondering at the golden disk of the moon telling a story of loveliness to every child that turned a head to glance at her.

No Peter Pansy came flying in at her windows—the curtains were a little too thick for that young man—to whisk her off to a never, never land, turning things that were not into things that were, instead of turning things that were into things that were not ; no Winnie the Pooh gambolled in her garden ; instead her fancies were formed from the brown wind of Connaught, soft in summer ; in winter, fierce, sending the foam from the waves, beating the Galway coast, flying over the land, covering her window with its healthy bitter brine. And in the midst of the breeze or blast she learned of the deeds of Cullin's Hound, listening with a wide-open ear to her nurse, Mary Sheridan, telling tremendous tales of him who swore by the oath of his people that 'he would make his doings be spoken of among the great doings of heroes in their strength.' So he did, and so did she. Is it not all written down by her in the fine gay book called *Cuchulain of Muirthemne* ? It's well we can see her, she sitting up in her big bed, her hair chained up for the night, her firm lips half open, her eyes intent on fancied glories, that Mary Sheridan's seeding words set out before her, of warriors, sages, stately queens, trancing the young girl into seeing Maeve, great Queen of Cruachan, fixed, fine and haughty, in the best red-repp chair of Roxborough, and she listening to the bronze-ribbed chariots of the Red Branch Knights thundering by in the woods outside.

She lived her young life, and rose out of the red repp and yellow plush life of the period : plush-covered photo frames, plush-covered bodies and furniture, plush-covered faith in God, and a plush-carpeted heaven to parade about in when the soft day's work was done. She says somewhere that 'as a child in the drawing-room, I kept silent, the elders, between piano-playing and newspapers, kept to themselves the little conversation there was, while I, sitting at the fireless side of the round table, read the few books that lay there' ; a habit she kept by her, for evenings, whenever possible, found her with a book in her hand which she read herself, or to some visitor whom she liked and was glad to have beside her.

That she questioned is certain, and that she felt another life, wider, mightier, and harder than her own around her, is certain, too ; for of all those who were with her when her busy literary and dramatic life began, she alone sat among the plain people, safe at ease, and they sat safe at ease with her. George Moore rarely had the heart to stray beyond the border of his Aubusson carpet ; and when he did so, got lost, and hurried back to the safe and soft terra firma, to give thanks for a safe and speedy deliverance to his holy Manet Icon hanging on the wall ; poor old clumsy-minded Edward Martyn, lurching round in the shadows of his ta ra ra Gothic house, pumping Palestrina out of an harmonium, had clothed the world's life in a clergyman's cassock, saw naught but what the dim light of a holy candle showed him, clutched like a vice in his damp and pudgy hand, living his life like a colourless moth fluttering between the finger and thumb of a portly priest ; W. B. Yeats heard something strange at times, as his letter defending the workers in 1913 showed, cocked an uneasy ear, didn't like what he heard, shuddered, and chanted,

All things uncomely and broken, all things worn out and old,
The cry of a child by the roadway, the creak of a lumbering cart,
The heavy steps of the ploughman, splashing the wintry mould,
Are wronging the image that blossoms a rose in the deeps of my heart.

Shocked he was, and a little frightened, so he turned to run, chanting,

Come away, O human child !
To the waters and the wild,
With a faery, hand in hand,
For the world's more full of weeping than you can understand.

But Lady Gregory wasn't afraid of the child's cry by the roadside, or the creak of a lumbering cart. She spoke warm words to the ploughman splashing his weary way homewards. She trotted smilingly beside all these things, sad or merry, listened to their tales, sang songs with them when they were cheerful and mourned with them when they were sad ; felt the good warmth of the fine turf fire on her feet, and emptied the sorrows of her own heart into the sorrow of others. Out of her plush and peplum she came to serve the people, body and mind, with whatever faculties God had given her.

AWAY WE SCOOTED from Gort, on a jaunting-car, she on one side, I on the other, with John, her coachman, sitting on the crampy seat in front, a good leg over one side of the horse's rump and a stiff one hanging over the other, whipping up the game little animal into a trot-gallop for Coole, so that I might have time for a wash before the dinner came to the table. A long sweeping drive gave a ceremonial path to the house, which shone out, here and there, in hand-broad patches, from a blue sky, through thronging trees, ripe in age, and kingly in their branchiness. Past the front we went, a long, wide, yellowish-white simple Georgian building, with many windows, a big, manly-looking entrance, tightly shut now for many years, facing what was once a curving expanse of green loveliness, but was now a gay gathering of primrose and violet, making themselves at home where once prime ministers, statesmen, and governors, with their silk-gowned and parasolled women, strolled over the velvety green grass, with grace and charm manœuvring the poor world about to their own sweet liking.

Lady Gregory was a Connaught woman, knowing every foot of the province, and every story told by every bush and stone in the counties of Galway and Clare ; and she showed her Connaught rearing by compelling her seventy odd years to climb down, like a stiff gazelle, from the high seat of the side-car, running into the house by a side door, turning, stretching out her two hands, to say with a beaming smile, One and twenty welcomes, Sean, to the old House of Coole !

Mistress of a grand house, filled a little too full with things brought from the four quarters of the round earth, some of them that would bring the ghosts of Victorians hovering around, and others, more modern, that would send them moaning off again ; a huge gleaming white marble figure of Andromeda in the drawing-room, brought there, she said, because its white nakedness had shocked the finer feelings of the people when it was outside ; the really glorious library, walled with precious books in calf and vellum, most of them forgotten, still murmuring in Greek, Latin, and Sanscrit against the changing tempo of the reading world. Here was a house that for a century had entertained great people as well as tinkers and tailors ; for every old or young fiddler passing through South Galway came to patronise Coole, receiving honour and largesse, after playing, maybe, *Leather the Wig*, or *The Soft Deal Board* ; making me imagine, as I went upstairs (the walls covered with mezzotint and engraving, so that, without knowing it, you passed by half the history of England), or strolled through the rich rooms, that I heard the bright dancing notes of *The Blackberry Blossom* flowing from an old fiddle, mingling with the voice of Yeats sonorously chanting out of him *The Wild Swans at Coole*.

In the library o' nights, heavy curtains pulled taut, a blazing log fire in a huge open grate, I stretched out cosy in a deep settee ; she, from the gentle aura of candlelight, read me Hardy's Epic-Drama of the War with Napoleon, in Three Parts, Nineteen Acts, and One Hundred and Thirty Scenes ; and soon I found myself battling sleepily for dear life to keep awake and hear what the Spirit of the Years, the Spirit of the Pities, the Spirit of Rumour, the Shade of the Earth, and Spirits Ironic and Spirits Sinister had to say to me. The poem seemed to have been begun in the Dark Ages, and that it would continue till the light of the sun went out ; while I (may the Mother o' God ask Her Son to pardon me) murmured that it was lovely when she paused for a rest, though conjuring her not to tire herself too much. However, the gentle woman made up for the strain by reading me *Moby Dick*, a reading I have never forgotten, and Hudson's *The Purple Land*.

One evening she came in with a surprise—a petrol lamp into which air was pumped so that it 'dave a light,' she said, 'dat made de night even as de day is on a noon of a summer morning.' There stood the lamp on a high stand on a high table, a lovely thing, with a silver-like stem and an opalescent shade. Lady Gregory's maid, Brigid, hovered around while her ladyship pumped air into the petrol bowl, anxiously watching, and murmuring, 'Let me give you a little hand with it, me lady' ; a kind offer that was met with the angry retort of 'Doh away, woman, doh away ; it's twite simple, and I tan handle it myself.' Turning to me, she added, 'And, now, Sean, you'll soon see a light dat never was on sea or land.' She was quite right, too, for as soon as she put a light to it, the thing gave out a mighty hiss that was half a scream, a bluish-white flame shot up high as the lofty ceiling, the old lady's face became as opalescent as the lampshade, and her wildly-puckered little mouth began sending puffs of harmless air towards the soaring flame, opening wide between the puffs to shout, 'Brigid, bring a blanket, bring a blanket, Brigid, before de house does up in flame !' I whipped up a rug from the settee, placing it between the flame and our faces for fear the thing would explode ; and behind this safety curtain we juggled and blew and smothered the thing till the fire sank down and died out, the three of us standing around it, dead silent, till it cooled, and Brigid could carry the soiled silver bowl and the cracked globe out of our sight into the kitchen.

'Oh !' she murmured, sliding down into the darkness of the settee, 'a punishment, a punishment on me for my banity ; tinking I could do it alone ; tinking I knew too much : oh ! the banity of it, the banity ! Back to de candles dat bring surety and peace and goodwill to all men, giving a sober light to all that are in de room.'

It was strange to watch that white, frightened look on that fine firm face, to realise that even Lady Gregory knew what fear was, shrinking from physical fire, though she walked calm through the ordeal of mental and spiritual fire when she fought the good fight for the freedom of the theatre against priest, peasant, politician, and Gaelic Leaguer howling high and low and long for the putting down of Synge and all the pomps and vanities of his wicked works, throwing their poisoned weapons, and shouting their holy and unholy war cries, like mad-made savages in a bewitched wood : against them all she stood, born, if not to rule the storm, to ride it, fighting it all out victoriously in Ireland's heart, and dipping into the battle again through the gigantic cities of the United States, choosing strife that was good rather than the loneliness of a false peace. Again, later on, she stood before Blanco Posnet, defending him against Dublin Castle, its robed Lord Lieutenant, its Pursuivant, Equerries, Men-at-arms, scrolls, parchment laws, and crests ; archer Shaw beside her, shooting many a stinging arrow of wit into the swarming foe, making them fall back and yelp and lower their banners and seek shelter in the hollows of the hills of silence.

Again, her banner of courage (a gay one, too) went up on the wind, when in 1903, on a day that brought Yeats, Florence Farr, Arthur Symons and others to take dinner with her, seeing a letter from home on the table, she took it to another room to read it quiet, finding that every line told of a new disaster, caused by the Big Wind of that year—lime trees flat, oaks, elms, pine, and larch had gone tumbling down, 'breaking demesne walls, blocking the public roads ; and the great ilex tree on the lawn, under which men and boys used to gather for our cricket matches,' gave up the ghost and fell and was no more. 'I said nothing to my guests,' she says, 'but read the play they came to hear ; and the work being *Riders to the Sea*, its tragedy suited my mood.'

When she got home again she didn't wail, but set out on a journey, seeking a sawmill ; and picked up a second-hand one somewhere, got suitable and unsuitable men to work it, and set it going, making all sorts of things for the convenience and comfort of the local people, selling them for cost price, cleverly coaxing evil into good, the good flowing wide and soundly out into the far distance ; for when I came to Coole the sawmill was still working at the remnants of the fallen timber.

I HADN'T BEEN ten minutes at the table before I was as if I had often been there before, she in simple and most gracious ways showing me how things were handled ; pointing out that 'Dese things were done, not because of any desire for ceremony, but because they made one more tomfortable, and made tings easier to eat.' So we were soon talking thirteen to the dozen, she, when she wanted something from the kitchen, snapping a finger against a tiny Burmese gong that gave a soft, plaintive, penetrating note, holding in its quivering sound the muted song and sadness of Burma. Passing through a room with the blue mountains of the Barony of Loughrea nodding in at the great bow windows, I was shown some of Coole's treasures ; and paused in front of a picture of a broad-shouldered young man, with an open and courageous face.

—My dear son, she murmured softly ; my dear, dear son ; lost leading his air squadron over de Italian battlefield. For months and months I had dreaded it, for I knew de German planes were ahead of ours.

I glanced aside, sympathetically at her, and saw that holy tears were trickling down the deep furrows of her tawny cheeks.

—Dear Lady, dear friend, I said softly, pressing her arm, the fall of a young man is a common thing now, and may be still a common thing in years to come ; a common thing for young and hopeful life to be cut down before it has had time to blossom and to shed its seed. It is for us who have been left standing to turn our thought into a way of deliverance from the cruel and wasteful banishment of our younger life, with all its lovely visions barely outlined, becoming, when they go, a tinted breath of memory.

She forced her head higher, murmuring, We must be brave, and fence our sorrow away so that no shadow may come upon those singing and dancing around us. Come, let us go for a walk in de woods.

The Seven Woods of Coole, with their many winding paths, so many that it behoved a rambler to go warily that he be not lost in the mazes among the trees. Sometimes a badger cut across our way, and red squirrels romped up and down the trees nearest the orchard, watching for the workers to go so that they might hop over the wall and steal the fruit. In working overalls, which were an old black dress, and a wide-brimmed old black straw hat, leather gauntlets over her able, wrinkled hands, one of which clutched a stout chisel-ended stick, she walked a little before me, or beside me when the going was good. Here, in the Wood of the Nuts, right in our path, callous and impudent, rose a mighty thistle, fully eight feet high, thrusting out its savage barbs towards our breasts, daring us to come on. It was then, with a fire of defiance in her eyes, the Old Lady, hissing angrily, would charge down on the foe, one gauntleted hand seizing a spiked branch, while the other stabbed the main butt of the thistle with the chisel end of the stick, till the branchy spikes tottered, bent back, and fell to the ground ; the victory celebrated by an uplifted stick and a fierce muttered 'So perish all de king's enemies !'

Occasionally, through the lusty leafiness of hazel and ash, we caught a silver glimpse of Coole river flowing by, a river that bubbled up suddenly from the earth in a lonely corner, alive with a luminous host of pinkish-blue and deeply-blue and proud forgetmenots ; diving under the ground again, after widening into a lovely lake on whose gentle bosom wild swans settled and wild swans rose, lifting up the noble head of Yeats to watch them—

> Scatter wheeling in great broken rings
> Upon their clamorous wings ;

possibly a little envious of them, and wishing, faintly, he was one, because—

> Their hearts have not grown old ;
> Passion or conquest, wander where they will,
> Attend upon them still.

Well, Yeats grew old and cursed the handicap of age ; but passion lingered with him till the last, and conquest went before him till he laid himself down to leave us.

Books and trees were Lady Gregory's chief charmers : the one nearest her mind, the other nearest her heart. She laboured

H

long and lovingly in the Woods of Coole. She hated rabbits and
squirrels only when they nibbled the bark from her young saplings.
It was she who first taught me to distinguish between the oak—
'the first tree dat God made'—the beech, elm, hazel, larch, and
fir. She'd march along, telling their names, the way an eager
nun would tell her beads. Away in a sacred spot, a magnificent
copper beech swept the ground with its ruddy branches, forming
within them a tiny dingle of its own. This was the sacred tree of
Coole. On its great trunk were carved the initials of the great
ones who had come to visit Lady Gregory's home, so that they
might 'be remembered forever.' The initials of Augustus John
were there, and those of Bernard Shaw and Yeats were cut deep
into the bark that looked like hardened dark-red velvet.

—What a lovely idea, piped a lady visitor one day, and she
staring at the tree. Show me your penknife, Sean, till I cut mine.

—You'll do noding of the sort ! came angrily from the Lady
of Coole, for dat dree is a dree dat grows for dreat people. Here,
let us doh back to de house ; and she lifted a sweeping bough to
allow passage to the ignorant visitor from the sacred grove
where great men worshipped and she was a wrinkled, new-born,
wary Vesta.

With all her bowing down before the mystery of great poetry
and great painting, she never left the sober paths trod into roughness by the feet of the common people ; as, after the proud
butchers of the locality had raised high the price of beef, se
bought cattle herself, found out men to kill and cut them up,
selling the meat to the people at fair prices, so that, a Kiltartan
man told me, and he stabbing towards the white clouds with the
stem of his pipe, 'Whenever me lady strolled through Gort, with
her eyes wide open an' her mouth tight shut, the boyo butchers
shrunk back, an' thrembled th' way you'd fair see a man shakin'
an' he on the gallows with a rope round his neck, knowin' there
was no deliverance from a lettin' down of their prices, knowin' all
that they were well bet to th' world.'

LADY GREGORY was busy making a Gort cake. Ah !
that was a busy time, for the cake was for a tea that she gave in
the green room to the Abbey actors whenever she came to Dublin.
Some of the actors elected to look on the cake with contempt ; but
they ate it all right, and when the tea was over, though the cake

would feed a regiment, I noticed there was never more than a little left : gone in the wind, I suppose. The cake was a rich thing of spice, currants, and raisins ; but rarest thing in its make-up was a noggin of purest brandy to help to damp the dough. It was a wet day, and I was standing before one of the great bow windows, watching the rain lashing down in silvery sheets over the saturated lawn ; and listening to the sighs of the great lime tree, disturbed by the sharp and sturdy wind that blew its branches to and fro. Suddenly I saw a dark figure, crouching to fight the wind and rain, slowly battling its way up the circling drive towards the big house.

—Derrible day, Sean, derrible ! said Lady Gregory, coming in to have a squint out at the weather.

—Whoever's coming up the drive, Lady Gregory, must feel that the day isn't as fine as it might be.

—Oh ! dat's Sammy Mogan coming to get some pension papers signed. De foolish man, de foolish old man, to tome on a day like dis !

She was gone in a second. I heard the bell of the side-door ring ; heard someone entering the hall, and then silence came. Tired of looking at the rain, I went slowly over the pictures hanging on the stairway wall. Out comes the old man to the hall, muffled up in a greatcoat, his eyes and nose only apparent, a bundle of soppy clothes under an arm, and he bidding the lady goodbye at every step he took.

—You must nebber come out on a day like dis again, Sam.

—What signifies it, me lady ? What's in it for a day but a harmless sup o' rain ? Soft as th' bloom on the cheek of Emer it is ; penethratin' though it is, it threats the skin quietly, like th' tendher touch of a mother bird's wing reachin' over the nest of her young ones. An' isn't th' cordial you've given me afther liftin' me into the powerful state of thinkin' th' heaviest rain on the coldest day in th' heart of winther to be nothin' but the soft petals of scented blossoms fallin' gently down from high-born branchy threes ? With th' form safe an' sure in me pocket, sure it's whistlin' a bar of a song I'll be all th' way home, intherspersed with prayers for seven blessins seven times a day on you, me lady, an' all who dwell in your hale an' generous house !

—Whisper, Sean, said Lady Gregory, as we went to the fire in the library, de Dort cake will lack its warm life dis time : he was so perished that I had to give him the noggin of brandy; and he whistled *The Blackberry Blossom* for me as a gift of tanks ! ✱

Sitting here in the garden, seeing the sun go down behind the garden wall and distant Burren hills, but giving Coole a red and gold salute before it goes, I realise that Lady Gregory, in the midst of her merriment and mourning with the Kiltartan people, is ever running round, a sturdy little figure in her suit of solemn black, gay-coloured by gleaming eyes and dancing smile, is ever running in and out of Yeats's Celtic Twilight, which she tells us herself she could never fully understand ; explaining, when she was asked about it, that 'it was a movement to persuade the Scots to begin buying our books, while we continued not to buy theirs '; turning his Rosa Alchemica into a homely herb ; and coaxing the wildness of his Red O'Hanrahan into the steady dancing of a hornpipe on the Abbey stage ; in her humorous and critical moods, swinging a critical lantern, she trespassed, too, into AE's Amethystine quarters of quivering peacock-tinted visions, where he was head low and heaven-bent and busy reporting Divine Orders, seeing things innumerable and unmentionable, beings plumed with red, white, green, blue, and orange flames ; where there were Brother-Selfs, Master Souls, Ancient Beauties, elfs, and faeries madly dancing a rigadoon a dad a derry o ; in she'd trot, her hand innocently pulling aside AE's curtains of purple twilight of half day and whole evening, half hiding the Pleroma, gone today and here tomorrow, to let in a little air on the dusky grandeur of the Great Breath's shadows, frightening into a flutter the dim moths of twilight trees, twilight hills, twilight men, twilight women, and twilight kids, crying out in her quiet way, through all the jamboree of twilight thought, that there were things to cook, sheets to sew, and pots and pans and kettles to mend.

It is very hard to single out the finest work done by Lady Gregory during the time of her activities with the literary and drama revival in Ireland, for she had as much to do with what she did not do as she had with what she did : whether it was the sympathy and lofty encouragement (not forgetting blue curtains for the window of his little flat, and other things) she gave to the great Yeats ; bringing him so often down from the city to *The Wind among the Reeds ;* leading him out so that his dreaming eyes could see *The Wild Swans at Coole* settling on or rising from the sunny waters of the Lake of Coole ; making the poet at home in the dignity, quiet, and comfort of a fine house, and soothing him with a sunny seat under a spreading catalpa tree in a sunny garden, where a summer evening was full of the linnet's wings : whether it was the warm determined will that gave the Irish Theatre more than a local habitation and a name—a world-wide name ; for nor Yeats, Edward Martyn, the brothers Fay, nor Miss Horniman gave the Abbey Theatre its enduring life, but this woman only, with the rugged cheeks, high Irish upper lip, twinkling eyes, pricked with a dot of steel in their centre ; this woman, only, who, in the midst of venomous opposition served as a general run-about in sensible pride and lofty humility, crushing time enough out of odd moments of rest from the toil of home and theatre to write play after play so that animated life kept passing to and fro, before the people, on the Abbey stage.

—Ah, dere you are, she said, coming up to me and pausing a moment watching the sun go down over the lands of the Kings of Burren. She went on to the long glass-walled vineries, and came back with a bunch of purple grapes for me. They had an imperial look, but were sour to the tongue and set my teeth on edge, though I managed to keep my face calm before her peering eyes, and murmur out that they were lovely.

—Oh ! what a job we had detting dem back to dood condition again ! she said.

An expert had tended the vines long ago, but he was expensive, and a common gardener, friend to Lady Gregory, had firmly volunteered to take the vines in charge. He was a man who had gone to a far country in one boat, coming back again in the next, nearly. He constantly chanted into her half-willing ear that he could tend them as well as the other fellow, ay, betther than anyone.

—Sam, Sam, deyre berry tender tings, and delicate to mind.

—Isn't that what I'm afther tellin' you all th' time, me lady ? Isn't it meself that knows more'n I'm able to tell about the figaries of growth in th' growin' o' grapes ? Th' one thing you've got to guard against, with their twistin' here an' their twistin' there, is not to lose your temper.

—Oh, it's more than dat, Sam ; it's more than a little loss of demper.

—Sure, don't I know that, me lady? Isn't that what I'm tellin' you all the time? That's only th' beginnin'; but a mighty fine beginnin'. You just keep your eyes off the grape threes, me lady, for a season or two, an' I'll go bail I'll bring you a crop of grapes, the like of which was never seen in this counthry since th' year o' one!

—I don't like de word crop given to grapes, said Lady Gregory; it doesn't seem a suitable name for the elegant purple fruit.

—Sure, it couldn't be more unsuitable, me lady; but suitable or unsuitable, it's a good name, an' has its meanin'. An' it's afther sayin' all this I am, th' way you'd hand th' grape threes over to a widely-minded man, who, in a foreign counthry, went knee-deep an' shoulder high through plants an' bushes growin' conthrary to th' methods of man, only showin' blossoms an' flingin' out fruit be th' dint of sthrivin' afther their knowledge an' their nursin'.

Hiding her doubts deep in her heart, she handed over the grape trees to Sam, and went away on a long, long journey. She came back, still doubtful, but confirming her faith in Sam by imagining grapes hanging thick in her vineries, more richly purple than ever, and puffing out their silken skins with the winey juice inside them.

—Well, how are de vineries? she asked of John, her coachman, driving her along the Gort road to Coole.

—What way would they be but thrivin', me lady? Be all accounts, they're growin' as they never grew before.

—Well, how are de vineries? she asked of Brigid, and she stepping in over the threshold of Coole.

—An' how would they be, me lady, but doin' grand? Be all accounts, they're growin' as they never grew before.

—I don't like dat phrase of dem growing as dey nebber grew before, said Lady Gregory, with a sparkle of anger in her eyes; it sounds too dood to be true. I'll run down to see dem, before I do anoder ting!

Off she went at a run to where they were; and there they were—a sight to see and a sight to remember: They had shot up like magic beanstalks; long, gaunt, angular stems, they had pushed everything aside in their hurry upwards, and had now lifted the glass roof a foot or more above the walls. Bare of fruit they were, and almost bare of leaf, desolate they looked and woebegone.

When the expert came again, he shook his head sadly.

—It will be long, me lady, before we can get them to start life all over again.

—Dat derrible man Sam ; oh ! dat derrible man ! And all of dem telling me dey were growing as dey nebber grew before.

—Looks as if they were right, said the expert.

ON A STONE WALL surrounding what was once, maybe, a meadow, but now a heath, I sat simmering in the sun. All over the heath the many wild plants were covered with mantles of brilliant blue butterflies. I had never seen so many anywhere before. In the garden, here and there, one, or, maybe, a pair, flew about from this flower to that one ; but here they were in tens of thousands ; as they settled and rose they looked like a multitude of blue banners carried by an invisible army. I wondered if Yeats had ever set eyes on them. Probably not, for this place was off his beaten way of rambling, and so these fairies, more lovely than anything seen by AE in dream or out of it, were denied the lyric their loveliness commanded. Wouldn't the Old Lady's deep black figure look grand among the brilliant blue ? Doing a slow, graceful, if a little stiff, minuet. A symbol of her dear courtesy, a quiet radiant pearl lying among her coloured qualities. Curiously kind to those she liked, or who helped her little theatre in any way. After Aubrey de Vere, the poet, ever hanging on to the coat-tail of Wordsworth, had said kind things to her and guaranteed a coin or two, had gone from Coole, didn't she climb a hillside of the Aughty mountains, all in the morning early, and read *The Excursion* from its weary beginning to its weary end ; to rise, finally, worn out, a few more grey hairs sparkling rudely in her head, after reading the last word of it as the sun was setting behind the faraway hills of Connemara ? That was her way, extending courtesy to one who had gone from her sight, satisfying her own warm heart by the hard performance.

It was a great day for Ireland, the day forty-three years ago, that saw Edward Martyn driving over to see the Count de Basterot at Duras by the sea in County Galway ; for Yeats was with Martyn, and Lady Gregory was staying with the Count. It came out to be a wet day, and a wet day in Galway, close to the sea, is a day for hardy mariners only to be out. So, after lunch, they had to stay in the house ; and the Count wanting to talk to Mr Martyn (possibly about rent ; for knights and pious persons don't always despise money), Lady Gregory piloted Yeats to another room, where they sat down, and she listened to him talking about the theatre, in which she wasn't at all interested. There they sat, with the rain streaming down the windows, their words mingling with the sound of the breakers foaming round the headland of Aughanish ; she saying—with her natural courtesy —that 'it was a pity there was no Irish theatre where Irish plays could be done ' ; he responding with 'an Irish theatre was the dream of his life.' One word borrowed another, till 'things seemed to grow possible as we talked, and before the end of the afternoon we had made our plan.'

There in that short sentence we have it all : she who had had no interest whatever in the theatre had come to look upon an Irish one as a necessity ; had made a plan ; for be sure it was in her quick and ready mind that the plan was born. She came to work in the theatrical vineyard at the eleventh hour, and from then, sank, or plunged, into the burden and heat of the day.

As well as writing hundreds of letters, helping in rehearsals, mediating in disputes, forging money from the lack of faith in others, minding her own business, she became foster-mother to some of Yeats's plays, weaving in dialogue for his *Cathleen ni Houlihan* and *Pot of Broth ;* helping the construction of *The King's Threshold* and *Where there is Nothing ;* throwing in, for good measure, scenarios from which Douglas Hyde, Eire's present President, made out *The Poorhouse* and *The Marriage.* An old Galway man once said of her, 'You have been a serving maid among us' ; and here, in the theatre, among the playwrights and poets—herself a better playwright than many of them—she was a serving-maid, too ; or, as Shaw called her, 'the theatre's char-woman' : a charwoman, right enough, but one with a star on her forehead. This serving eagerness was, I think, a weakness in her nature. She thought too much of the work of others, foaming out their own importance, leaving her but little time to think of her own. So a good deal of her work seems to show signs of hurry, hinting no matter if mine be not good so long as that of others be better ; though few of them were half as good, for she was a born dramatist, and, had she given the time to herself she gave to others, would, I believe, have died a great one.

One time, she became a little troubled by the pushing realism of the younger writers, sanely troubled, too ; for most of the realism was a foggy blackness over life, with, maybe, a little laugh squeezed into a corner, and more quickly squeezed out again, before anyone had time to hear it ; full of dim chatter, they were, with ne'er a scarlet thread of humour in it, nor a golden rose of joy. She tried to offset this realism by the creation of an historical play, arguing with herself that 'to come into the real life of the country, the theatre must touch a real and eternal emotion, and history comes only next to religion in Ireland.' She made many starts at a play about Brian Boru, called *Kincora*, hammering it out in spite of Yeats's advice to give it up ; and though she says 'it was received with some enthusiasm,' it wasn't in itself the success it might have been, and so hindered its welcome with critic and audience. It was a great pity that the woman was so close to Yeats while she was writing this play : he had a bad effect on her confidence in her own creation. He had no right to advise her to give up the effort ; but she served so frequently in so many common ways that Yeats easily dismissed from his mind her natural vigour in the creation of imaginative drama. Sometimes, too, high on his poetical throne, the world forgetting, an *ex cathedra* wave of a scornful hand dismissed everything save what was dissolving in the wonder of his own thoughts. It was a shame that the modelling of the play should have been chilled by the cold criticism of Yeats ; for great poet and greater man that he was, he never had the stuff of drama in him that she showed, glowingly, even in her first efforts to put plays on the stage. But her wonder plays and her folk-history plays will, when the mammonised theatre becomes the playhouse run by the people for the people, be honoured as her comedies now are.

THREE SORROWS were rifling her heart of peace when first came across her and founded a friendship with Coole. The tumbling burning death of her son, Major Gregory, was barely softened by her devotion to his three young children. This was a bitter blow to her, and a bad, but unnoticed, loss to Ireland ; for to his many qualities he added that of a fine, delightful, and sensitive designer to the theatre. His staging for *Kincora*, says Yeats, was 'beautiful, with a high grave dignity, and that strangeness which Ben Jonson thought to be part of all excellent beauty.' Though I have never seen these designs displayed, their description is enough to show their beauty plain ; and when Robert Gregory fell crashing on the hilly soil of Italy, Ireland may have lost an Irish, and more colourful, Gordon Craig.

The second sorrow was the Atlantic weaving with her waves a winding sheet for Sir Hugh Lane, her nephew, when he went down with the *Lusitania*, 'almost in sight of the house in which he was born in the County of Cork.' This was he who, in a dark room, with his eyes shut, could sense the presence of a Rembrandt or a Constable, hidden high up in a corner, and covered with the dust of years. He it was who, through heavy opposition, gave many gems of painting to many galleries, scattering these lovely things all over Dublin as another would scatter rose petals in the heat of a gay carnival. A loss he was, a great loss to his people, though only a very few felt it, besides the lonely woman in her house at Coole. To me, then, he was none ; I felt it not ; knew it not ; but know it well now.

Then there was the taking away of the Lane pictures from the ken of Dublin, a poisoned wound this, deep and angry. To her last breath she followed after them, seeking them, seeing them, and often I went with her. They are still exiled from their native home ; but they will be brought back. Though we were blind to their beauty, so were others, better placed than we ; for one of them, Renoir's *Umbrellas*, lay for a long time deep in the cellars of the National Gallery, too trivial for a hanging on a respectable wall. Be easy in your grave, dear lady ; they will come back again to us.

What shall we bring to the place where she lies sleeping ? A promise not to forget the Lane pictures ; some of the rich forgetmenots from the glade where the fresh river rises ; a branch of the copper beech bearing the cut-in initials of those who sat at her table and walked in her sunny garden ; an old fiddler to play *The Blackberry Blossom* ; the butterflies swarming like a blue banner, or, as she would say, like the blue mantle of Brigid ; a vine leaf or two, in token of her gay heart ; since she elected to

live and die a Christian, a cross ; and the voice of her friend
chanting—

> Here traveller, scholar, poet, take your stand
> When all those rooms and passages are gone,
> When nettles wave upon a shapeless mound
> And saplings root among the broken stone,
> And dedicate—eyes bent upon the ground,
> Back turned upon the brightness of the sun
> And all the sensuality of the shade—
> A moment's memory to that laurelled head.

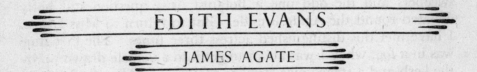

EDITH EVANS

JAMES AGATE

Some years ago, during one of my financial crises, a firm of
publishers offered me fifty pounds for a life of Rachel, of whom I
knew absolutely nothing. Now needs must when the Devil drives,
and three weeks later I delivered the MS. of a book of which Arnold
Bennett wrote that it was, and must remain, the last word in
English on the greatest of all actresses. History repeats itself. I
cannot remember whether, when the Editor invited me to contribute to THE SATURDAY BOOK, I was undergoing a financial
crisis or not. After all, to a man who is a chronic sufferer from
sick headaches, one date is very like another. In any case I
have known no time at which the offer of money has not instantly
produced from me the promise of an article, and the cash the
stuff. In this respect I have always been perfectly honest with
my editor. I never pretend to knowledge ; and when I don't
know I say so. One of the foibles of the cheaper kind of newspaper is to choose for its dramatic critic some young man who
has never been near the theatre and knows nothing whatever of
dramatic art. This is called 'the fresh mind.' Actually, since the
young man in question will not have a mind, it is bringing mere
freshness.

Now, I have known freshness do very well ; it did very well
in my life of Rachel. Let me hope that it will do as well in the
case of the lady about whom I have been asked to write, and of

whom, *off the stage* I know as little as I knew of Rachel on it. I have been told that Edith Evans began life as a humble seamstress, and with a bundle of sewing under her arm would walk, or take a bus, to some amateur dramatic society whose members she would proceed to dazzle with her wit and charm. I cannot vouch for this ; I can only hope it is true. Happily the world has lost some of that snobbishness which made Charles Dickens carefully conceal from the world that his grandfather was a butler and his grandmother a housemaid. I myself do not care who knows about my six or seven—I hope it was seven—great-great-uncles who swept crossings prior to being transported. Whether one swept crossings while six were sent abroad or whether six were sweepers and the odd one a Botanist, is a question still hotly debated round the Agate fireside. But to return to Miss Evans. I have met this distinguished actress three times. The first time was in a fog, when I was about to get into a vehicle drawn up by the kerb and a stage-voice familiar to me said, 'My cab, I think.' The second time was at the Kean Centenary Celebration at Drury Lane, when we agreed that it was a fine day and that Edmund had been a fine actor. The third time was at the Ivy when Miss Evans asked me my views about reviving *The Late Christopher Bean*, and I said I would much rather she chose a piece called *I Serve*, this being the first piece in which I saw her. Miss Evans, with a glittering smile, said that on the whole she was tired of housemaids. This completes my knowledge of the subject of this article. I have heard her alluded to as Joe, or possibly Jo. Some aver that she is a Christian Scientist, and it is whispered that she is also an ardent Coué-ist who stands in the wings saying, before each and every entrance—

> Oh, I am fairer than the evening air
> Clad in the beauty of a thousand stars ;

I agree that, gazing round the glamorous field of present-day actresses, when it comes to style and the ravishingly impertinent suggestion of beauty, all is dross that is not Editha. The name in its Latin form stands for 'rich gifts.' Nothing could be happier.

I had a trifle of editorial difficulty with my *Rachel* book. This was that I had forgotten to fit the great actress into a series of 'Representative Women.' Now the book had begun with the most matter-of-fact statement as to the date on which Elisa Félix

was born. And then I had to start all over again and add something, the editor of the series insisting on this or alternatively
demanding the return of the fifty pounds which, of course, was
already spent. But difficulties exist to be overcome, and I added
a preliminary chapter which began, 'A "representative" woman?
Yes, I suppose Rachel represents her day and the theatre of her
day in the sense that anybody casting an eye upon the French
stage of the second quarter of the nineteenth century would be
bound to think first of Rachel. But to suggest that the most
famous of all tragédiennes is in any way representative of the
great dramatic movement which sprang up in her time would
be to suggest something essentially false. A great actor or actress
may be set in a period and identified with it without belonging to
that period. It does not follow because a mouse and a trap are in
the same room that the mouse must be inside the trap.'

Is Edith Evans a representative woman? And if so, whom
does she represent? I find it difficult to believe that this distinguished player has ever represented anybody except herself; or
at most the dramatist in whose piece she has been engaged to
play. There is no golden rule in this matter. Rachel made her
first appearance in 1837 and her last in 1855, and though these
years saw the rise and growth of the new Romantic Drama,
Rachel's only concern with that movement was to turn her back
on it. Anyone asked to name the most famous actor and actress
on the English stage during the latter half of the nineteenth
century would, I assume, have no hesitation in naming Henry
Irving and Ellen Terry. Equally it will not be disputed first,
that this partnership saw the beginning of the greatest revival of
dramatic energy in this country since the age of Elizabeth, and
second, that the partnership stood aloof from it. He who should
write a book round these two famous players will have nothing to
say of the new intellectual movement begun in 1891 by the
Independent Theatre, and whoever writes of the new drama in-
augurated by George Bernard Shaw will not mention these players.
On the other hand there are English actresses whom one definitely
identifies with certain theatre moods. Names like Florence
Farr, Elizabeth Robins, Janet Achurch and Mrs Patrick Campbell.
All these actresses were identified with the Ibsen movement, and
their stage story is largely the story of Nora Helmer, Rebecca
West, Hedda Gabler, Hilda Wangel, Gunhild Borkman, Ella

Rentheim, Rita Allmers, Asta Allmers, the Rat Wife and many others. Miss Evans has never identified herself with any dramatist in particular, and her essays in Ibsen, Shaw and Brieux have all been strictly in the way of business. She is an actress pure and simple. All has been fish that has come to her net, and the catch has been remarkable in its variety.

THERE ARE THOSE who claim to have seen Evans at her first appearance in the summer of 1912 as Cressida in the Elizabethan Stage Society's revival of *Troilus and Cressida*. They are largely the people who claim to have seen the Indian Rope Trick, the Sea-Serpent and the Loch Ness Monster. One of the first characters in which I had the felicity of seeing her was the repressed daughter of Brieux's Mons. Dupont, and I still remember the straining of that urgent bust against its sheath of black satin. Then followed a tour with Ellen Terry and half-a-dozen London appearances which in 1921 culminated in Lady Utterwood in Shaw's *Heartbreak House*. I had joined the *Saturday Review* in the September of that year and my sixth article was devoted to this play. I find that I wrote, 'Miss Edith Evans showed insight and enormous competence.' And then came the memorable day in September of the following year, when I saw our leading actress in what was, apart from Cressida, her first leading rôle. How well I remember it. I had not intended to go to the play that afternoon. Passing the Kingsway Theatre the Wemmick-like thought came into my head : 'Here's a play-house ; let's go in.' So in I went, to the sparse-filled pit. I had no programme and knew nothing of play or cast. A forebodingly comic plumber was mending a grate, while a maid-servant was answering the door up-stage. She turned round, and I recognised that the actress was Edith Evans. From that moment this exquisite player held not only me but all that handful of audience in thrall as poignant as that in which, years ago, George Moore had held us with *Esther Waters*. That novel was a masterpiece ; this little play was to tremble too often on the brink of absurdity. Yet there was to be found in it that which was both moving and true. At the fall of the curtain I went home and wrote, 'Miss Evans's Kate is the most finished piece of acting on the London stage to-day, perfect both spiritually and in externals, whether as the ultra-ladylike maid, or as the slightly vulgar *châtelaine*. It is the portrait of a great artist who possesses the gift of observation, a fine sense of comedy and the pathos of Mrs Kendal. The end of the tragi-comedy found the house in tears, with one exception. I had shed all of mine in the earlier acts, in sheer joy at so much beauty and felicity.' Three months later I found Miss Evans starring in a flashy little piece called *The Laughing Lady*, by Alfred Sutro, in which, for no reason, I remember that the name of the character enacted by Miss Evans was Cynthia Dell. 'Adultery? Nonsense!' said some plethoric Colonel, 'they never left the drawing-room!' 'You dear, old-fashioned darling,' gurgled Cynthia, 'I love you for that!' Turning up my newspaper cutting books I find that I wrote, 'Here let me break off to declare that Miss Edith Evans is the most brilliant and accomplished of English actresses. She may not have Miss Thorndike's power, but she has compensating pathos, a scarifying amount of brains, and an unrivalled comic instinct. Her Cleopatra was a Lely of exquisite distinction; her Cynthia is a Hogarthian grimace at the social butterfly. She is, oh so radiantly common! Her dress of clamorous iridescence no more contains her impudent, firm flesh than the gold-coloured pupa contains the emergent moth. Cynthia resembles the female of the Purple Emperor in that, in alimentation, she prefers the vitiated. This piece of mockery is like a child's "transfer" gaudily applied to a Lely engraving; it is magnificent.'

The actress had now made herself, but she had also come somewhere near to being made by the critics, which is a very different and possibly a more important matter. There was no doubt about it when at the Lyric, Hammersmith, in February, 1924, under the auspices of the Stage Society, she gave the theatre what is possibly its best Millamant. Her countenance was replete, as was said of Congreve's style, 'with sense and satire, conveyed in the most pointed and polished terms.' Her acting was 'a shower of brilliant conceits, a new triumph of wit, *a new conquest over dullness*.' Her Millamant was impertinent without being pert, graceless without being ill-graced. She has only two scenes, but what scenes they are of unending subtlety and finesse! Never can that astonishing 'Ah! idle creature, get up when you will' have taken on greater delicacy, nor 'I may by degrees *dwindle* into a wife' a more delicious mockery. '*Adieu*, my morning thoughts, agreeable wakings, indolent slumbers, all ye *douceurs*,

ye *sommeils du matin, adieu'*—all this was breathed out as though it
were early Ronsard or du Bellay. And 'I nauseate walking,' and
'Natural, easy Suckling !' bespoke the very genius of humour.
There was a pout of the lips, a jutting forward of the chin to
greet the conceit, and a smile of happy deliverance when it was
uttered which defied description. The actress's face, at such
moments, was like a city in illumination. One fault I found, and
one only. Millamant's first entry ought to bear out Mirabell's
announcement : 'Here she comes, i'faith, full sail, with her fan
spread and her streamers out.' Miss Evans made her appearance
something lapwing fashion, a trifle too close to the ground. It is
possible, too, that Mrs Abingdon gave the whole character a bigger
sweep ; Evans conceived her as a rogue in porcelain, and kept
her within that conception.

Three years later our actress reappeared at the same theatre in
another Restoration comedy, this time as Mrs Sullen in Farquhar's
The Beaux' Stratagem. The last production of this play on the
grand scale had been in 1879, at which period English playwrights
seem to have been considerably exercised as to the propriety of
revivals. Thus we find Boucicault writing, 'I no more desire to
see the defunct dramatist occupying the stage than I wish to see
my grandfather rise out of his respected tomb and reclaim my
inheritance.' To which a critic of the period retorted that not
everyone was in a position to regard the public stage as his own
private property. This particular revival appears to have been
a low-spirited affair, largely marred by the fact that the part of
Mrs Sullen was entrusted to a soubrette instead of an actress
possessed of the grand manner. The part was originally played
by Mrs Oldfield, and I remember wondering whether an actress
living in the first years of the eighteenth century could have had
her successor's exquisite period-sense. The answer, surely,
must be in the negative. To Oldfield 1707 was not a period but
the time of day, and Mrs Sullen was to be seen in any box at
Covent Garden. Given that the earlier actress's emotional,
intellectual, and æsthetic equipment was equal to that of her
successor, to what extent can the two performances have been
identical ? For Evans brought to the part more than faithfulness ;
she brought also a knowledge of that which only a very few years
ago it was fashionable to call emancipation, and an implication
of the altered relation between the sexes. No actor, though he be

steeped in Pirandello to the very lips, can make Aimwell and Archer other than the high-spirited sparks of Farquhar's imagining. Was it fancy, reason, or the intoxication of the delighted senses which, as we gazed at the new Mrs Sullen, made one see her double ? Did not Evans set beside her literal presentation something which we might call a critical estimate, a revision of the character as seen through modern eyes ? Did she not bring to the modish ornament a delicacy and perception which were no part of the feminine equipment of Farquhar's day ? Take her very first words. Dorinda says, 'Morrow, my dear sister ; are you for church this morning ?' I find it hard to believe that Oldfield's 'Anywhere to pray' can have had behind it an impertinence, malice, and scorn which would not have been out of place in the mouth of Clara Middleton or any other six foot of Meredithian womanhood preparing to leg it healthily to her devotions over six miles of hill and dale. Must not the eighteenth century actress have filled with a sense of present injury the passage beginning, 'O, sister, sister ! If ever you marry, beware of a sullen, silent sot,' instead of informing it, as Evans did, with the amused recollection of a chatteldom that is past ? The love-scene with Archer was played with the last refinement of wit and spirit, and it was a pin-still house which marvelled as the actress breathed out the closing passage, 'Look'ye, sister, I have no supernatural gifts—I can't swear I could resist temptation ; though I can safely promise to avoid it ; and that's as much as the best of us can do.' I will vouch for it that there was an emotion here which the dramatist never glimpsed.

Nine years later the actress again returned to her early love, Restoration comedy. This time she chose Lady Fidget in Wycherley's *The Country Wife*. Even the sternest moralist watching this performance must have balanced the merry quality of the riot against the lack of squeamishness. Personally, I do not believe that a committee consisting of Martin Luther, John Calvin, John Knox, William Penn, George Eliot, Mrs. Humphry Ward, and Mrs Ormiston Chant would have been able to resist the tremendous fun with which Evans invested Lady Fidget's indiscretions. The word pulls one up, since it has an accidental implication, and there is nothing of accident about Lady Fidget. Her sallies are all sorties directed against circumspection, wilfully planned. Here I venture to quote myself in the *Sunday Times*,

I

'Evans may have faults, though I have never been able to discover any. Upon a review of the whole range of her talents I will venture to affirm, as an early dramatic critic wrote, "That *impartial* JUSTICE *must* pronounce MISS EVANS as the *First* of her PROFESSION; and that the *amazing* BLAZE of her EXCELLENCIES greatly *obscures,* if not totally *eclipses* her DEFECTS." This was written, with the alteration of pronouns, about Garrick.'

Steadily and resistlessly Evans made a reputation for versatility, in which quality she has exceeded any other English actress. Let us look at one or two of her creations. I remember her Nurse in a production of *Romeo and Juliet* in which Romeo could not speak his part, Juliet was not up to acting more than half of hers, and Mercutio was a spineless creature lacking virility. Then came Evans to knock the balance of the play into a cocked hat, as would happen if the Porter were the centre of *Macbeth.* She ruled the entire roost. Obviously of the German-Flemish school, this was Hugh Walpole's Agatha Payne metamorphosed into good instead of bad angel. It was a grand performance, and taught young playgoers what pathos was in younger days. Now let me consider her Arcadina in *The Seagull.* When Miriam Lewes played the part she gave the fascinating creature a baleful, Strindbergian quality, largely because Lewes is good in Strindberg. A gifted colleague wanted Arcadina to have 'that element of persuasive pity with which Tchehov enriched the character and made it credible.' But this was because this particular critic could not conceive femininity shorn of the finer aspects of womanhood. Now, in my view, Evans in the character was exactly right, for the reason that she put nothing whatever into it that did not belong to it. If a baleful tigerishness had been the thing, she had only to turn on a bit of Agatha Payne. But she resisted the temptation, and her pacing up and down the room had the right amount of bad temper, and no more. On the other hand, if an ethereal quality had been wanted, the actress had only to turn on Gwenny in the play about the artist, or some other housemaid in act of oblation. But this, again, would not have been Arcadina, who held Constantin by the mere fact of being his mother, and Trigórin by her sex. Reading the scene very carefully, I cannot find one single syllable of the Duse-like quality of ennoblement. Arcadina is a well-known actress ; Trigórin a well-known novelist. The liaison is notorious and a good advertisement for both. She has got used to him, at forty-three doesn't want the bother of looking for somebody else, and is not going to have her nose put out by a ninny who goes in for amateur theatricals. Her re-conquest of her lover is a sordid business, skilfully and conscientiously carried through, and as no actress is ever quite good enough to play a scene perfectly without feeling a bit of it, towards the end Arcadina takes on some show of sincerity. And then, what a witty piece of acting Evans made it, taking the eye like a drawing of Sarah by Toulouse-Lautrec, and incidentally reproducing Sarah's coiffure, *circa* 1895, and the saucy little skiffs and sloops which, *circa* 1895, Sarah used for hats. A lovely performance of shimmer and sparkle, and quite rightly without one atom of heart to it !

HOW GREAT or how good an actress is Evans? At the fall of the curtain on the revival of Dekker's *The Witch of Edmonton*, Michel St.-Denis said, 'It is a pleasure to work with Miss Edith Evans, who is a great actress. She is a great actress in a great way. Not only does she transform herself every time, but all her transformations are convincing.' What is this but a re-statement of the opening sentence in G. H. Lewes's essay on Edmund Kean, 'The greatest artist is he who is greatest in the highest reaches of his art.' This brings us back to the charge against Bernhardt that she was always Bernhardt, against Irving that he was always Irving, but not for some odd reason to any charge against Duse that she was always Duse. Exactly the opposite is true. There were half a dozen Bernhardts, and at least a dozen Irvings. Anybody who ever thought that Sarah in Racine's Phèdre, in Hugo's Doña Sol, in Dumas's Marguerite, and in Maeterlinck's Pelléas was the same woman is a multitudinous ass. As for Irving, don't take my word, take Max's. Irving may not have been able to transform himself, and about this Max wrote, 'Irving's voice, face, figure, port, were not transformable.' But mark what follows, 'Intransformable, he was—multi-radiant, though.' Which means that though all the parts were Irving, they were not the same Irving. Which, again, means that there were always enough Irvings to go round. As for Duse, I really do not know. Max's 'prevailing impression' is that of 'a woman over-riding, with an air of sombre unconcern, plays, mimes, critics and public.' There is a legend of gaiety and the right kind of unconcern when

she played Mirandolina in Goldoni's comedy, and I myself
remember being simultaneously dazzled and saddened by her
Adrienne Lecouvreur. Here it occurs to me that an actress who
can do these two things at the same time must be in the way of
greatness. But then came a time when Duse took to dazzling
with grey hair and saddening with grey face, and so gave one the
excuse for thinking that an actress capable of playing Marguerite
Gautier in this monotonous guise was mistaking guff for sublimity.
Why not say that Sarah sometimes not herself, Irving always
grandly himself, and Duse, at least in her later years, sombrely
and resolutely herself, were all three great players? More
important, perhaps, is to discover the justification for saying so.
Because—and this is the great point—because each of them
possessed, and would in any evening of the week and given the
right play offer triumphant proof that he or she possessed, that
quality which Frederick Myers said was characteristic of Homer—
'the sense of an effortless and absolute sublimity.' Even Mr
Shaw, who throughout his critical career attacked Irving un-
ceasingly, admitted when he was dead that the old man had been
not only eminent, but pre-eminent. And no player can be
pre-eminent who does not suggest this effortless and absolute
sublimity. Equally, the player who can do this at once passes
into the strict and narrow rank of great actors. With this proviso,
that sublimity must be exhibited in the sublime ; the thing is not
achieved when an actress peers over the edge of a teacup Bergner-
wise and suggests an oblation to the gods. Let oblating be done
in the grand manner. Duse, Bernhardt, Irving all oblated.

Evans oblated when as a Welsh housemaid in *The Late Christopher Bean* she washed up the tea-things and yet contrived to look
like a canvas of Perugino. But if sublimity were all, acting would
be a dull business. And multitudinous asininity would be that
man's who thought that Gwenny and Agatha Payne in *The
Old Ladies* (April 1935) were the same woman. 'A slow nightmare
of macabre genius . . . some insane doll that increases continu-
ously in physical stature and spiritual decay,' wrote Mr Morgan.
Next came Juliet's Nurse (October 1935). 'As earthy as a potato,
as slow as a cart-horse, and as cunning as a badger,' wrote Mr.
Darlington of this. Her Lady Fidget in *The Country Wife* (October
1936) was 'a Rowlandsonesque cartoon of Britannia turned
bawdy,' wrote somebody. Next Rosalind (November 1936),

and I find that I was moved to write about 'bubbling seas of Renaissance wit.' As for her witch in Dekker's play, this was 'just good, straightforward melodramatic Mother Shipton plus a note of heart-searching pity which brings you up sharp in the middle of cruelty's guffaw.'

Very well then. Here we have an actress who can be macabre, doll-like, and insane, suggest the cart-horse, the potato, and the badger, make oblation to the gods, imply a bawdy cartoon, and at the same time ride bubbling seas of wit. If that is not versatility, then we must find a new Lewis Carroll to tell us what is. Mark finally that during the thirty years Evans has been on the stage not once has she repeated herself. Recalling Cressida with whom she began, Rebecca West (*Rosmersholm*), the woman in *Heartbreak House*, the singer in *Eventide*, Millamant, Sullen, Fidget, the repressed daughter of M. Dupont, the Serpent and the She-Ancient, Madame Arcadina, Florence Nightingale and Lady Bracknell, one cannot doubt that Evans must take rank as a great comic actress. Is she a great actress in the sense of effortless and absolute sublimity? If not, it is only because Nature has denied her the tragic mask.

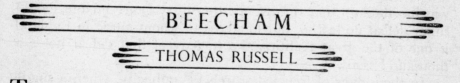

BEECHAM

THOMAS RUSSELL

The Fates must have laughed in April 1879 when they chose the medley of qualities which were to go to the make-up of Sir Thomas Beecham. The delicacy and refined taste of the miniaturist—and the trumpeted blatancy of the modern advertiser; the skill and cunning of an eighteenth century diplomat—and the fiery impatience which smashed all obstacles; the wit and eloquence of an Oscar Wilde—and the stubborn inability to understand what was obvious to the first-comer; the serious reverence for a great artist—and the frivolous disregard of the claims of an even greater one; the upholder of artistic traditions—and the anarchic despiser of modern conventions; a sincere patriot—but not his country's best advocate : all these qualities were selected for a lifetime of jostling incongruity.

Not satisfied with such careless generosity, the Fates ordained that these conflicting talents should be bestowed upon a human being of delicate proportions, but great staying power, destined never to exceed a bare five feet of stature, yet redeeming this last by giving him a handsome head, brilliant expressive eyes, and the most persuasive manner in the world. To cap it all, they placed this rare creature against a background of twentieth century industrial England—he was born at St. Helen's—against a wall of solid Philistinism, choosing for a parent the wealthy purveyor of a humble household requisite.

It is to this background that Beecham owes his significance. Imagine a long stretch of brick wall, easily found on the outskirts of any money-making town in this country ; the drab, despairing symbol of the minds which created it. In front of it stands a brilliant, scarlet-cloaked figure, with a Richelieu beard, a gallant poise, and a finely tempered sword in his hand. Shattering gestures, dauntless defiance and defence of a lost cause ; there you have the essential Beecham, and even though the Richelieu beard has to compete with a bowler hat, and the brilliant cloak has become the dull garb of today, and only the conductor's baton remains to suggest a Toledo weapon too fine for modern usage, the impression remains. That the brick wall should win was inevitable ; that the twentieth-century Don Quixote should suffer defeat no less so, but for those to whom music in England is one of the great realities, the tragedy of that defeat holds a thousand lessons.

In these days of frenzied search for publicity, when a single incident or a single broadcast may turn a man into a national figure, the household quality of Sir Thomas Beecham's name does not, of itself, guarantee a corresponding greatness behind it. His inherited good fortune, and the baronetcy he later acquired, would have opened an easy way to fame, even without the gifts of which he was the undeniable possessor. With them he could have graced the political scene, where he might have made no less a mark than did Richard Sheridan ; he might have become as outstanding a diplomat as Lord Curzon. But behind his talents lay an unquenchable desire. Another man with those particular gifts of mind, money and position might have become no more than the typical representative of a decayed generation, content to satisfy the enthusiasms of a lost youth by a pleasant pandering with one or other of the arts. And this was frequently his pose, and one which shook the earnest, Nonconformist conscience which lies not too deep in the English outlook. But the reality in Beecham lay deeper. He had a purpose. He had a purpose which burned and glowed in all he did, and that was still to be seen and felt when despair and cynicism drove him to words which seemed foolish or dangerous to those who accepted them at their face value. In a different generation and in a different country he might have settled to a steady career in any one of a number of spheres ; but growing to maturity in a period of transition he could not escape the struggles which were inherent in his changing world, struggles which had to be endured before the constructive phase in which his ideas could be realised had been reached. So it is against the background of an epoch that he must be seen ; sharpening the blade of his genius against the stone of opposition.

BEECHAM'S MUSICAL SYMPATHIES began early, nurtured as they were in a home where every inducement was offered for a closer acquaintance with music. Dame Ethel Smyth writes charmingly of this in her sparkling, if not always accurate, book, *Beecham and Pharaoh* ; she describes his childhood in a house full of 'every sort and kind of musical instrument,' and goes on to say that 'chiefly am I possessed by the idea of this abnormally gifted little creature, let loose, a mere baby, among all these instruments ; fingering them, if they were of the ancient hurdy-gurdy type turning the handles, listening by the hour to the disgorgings of the orchestrion, and incidentally getting on terms with a vast proportion of musical literature.' As he grew older his talent developed with his desire for self-expression, and although his early attempts often awakened some amusement among orchestral players, and did little to shake critics and the *cognoscenti*, that talent continued to develop until quite recent years. But Beecham had not only public favour to conquer. His most constant critic was himself. From the very first he had to convince himself of his gifts, and to satisfy himself time after time of his power to realise them. Psychologists could no doubt find an explanation for this driving desire for self-approval, from which so much that is characteristic of Beecham sprang. They might speak of his diminutive stature, of his name and, most of all, of the shameful knowledge that he belonged to a country branded for two centuries or more as unmusical. They might sum all this up as a case of inferiority complex, a motive force which has compelled much genius to achievement. At any rate, many of those who knew him were misled by his arrogance, or by his apparent belief in autocratic powers. Ethel Smyth seems to have made a mistake of this order when she says in the book mentioned above :

'There was a concert at St. Helen's, and he, aged eight, was to play in public for the first time. Walking on to the platform, he became suddenly aware of hundreds and hundreds of people . . . and absolutely lost all consciousness of what he was doing. He got through his piece, however, without a stumble and left the platform, still in a state of coma. Loud applause . . . but the child refused to go on again. Cajoled, shoved, scolded, at last he relented, and as he went on took a good look at the audience and discovered they were not dragons but just the ordinary people you see daily in the shops and streets. Then, yielding to the applause, he played again with the utmost composure, and from that day to this has never known what nervousness meant.'

As an example of over-simplification this can hardly be beaten, and the voice of the hero can be unmistakably heard. Even if the incident were true, its effect can have been no more than temporary, for during my acquaintance with him I have been constantly impressed by the many indications of nervousness before a concert, especially when the programme contained a work with which he was not at home. For an artist with such an emotional response to music this is inevitable. Sir Thomas might be the last to admit the truth of this, thus accounting for the story quoted above, and at such times he was always at great pains to display a sang-froid which comported ill with his own feelings. I have witnessed more than one exhibition self-devised to dispel his fears. At the final rehearsal for the first performance of the Bloch violin concerto, Sir Thomas, to whom many modern works make little appeal and therefore offer difficulties, found himself faced with a serious task. When, a few hours later, we were sitting on the Queen's Hall platform waiting for zero hour, the conductor walked on in his stiffest and most uncompromising manner. It was apparent to those whose business it was to watch him closely that he was as near panic as anyone with his long experience could be, and we looked forward to a stormy passage. The audience had not quite settled itself, and Beecham stood idly on his rostrum, fidgeting slightly. Suddenly, with no hint that could have been detected, he whipped round to face the audience, pointed an accusing finger at the stalls, and said loudly, 'Madam, smoking is not allowed in this hall.' It is said that a woman almost collapsed, and later had to leave, but I am prepared to believe that at that moment no one was guilty. Be that as it may, Sir Thomas turned back to the Orchestra completely transformed ; all trace of nervousness had vanished, he was altogether master of himself, and with that act of public self-assertion all danger of breakdown had gone. Speech has always been Beecham's safety-valve, and he was most silent when he was most at ease and self-composed.

Behind the self-criticism which produces this nervous approach to his work lies the seriousness of the artist, and this was hidden with such care that those who knew him only superficially were willing to believe that he looked upon conducting an orchestra as nothing more than good fun. He would go a long way to convince the world that his scores were never prepared and that his most marvellous effects were gained on the spur of inspiration. That this was not true could be recognised by any orchestral player who had studied the meticulous accuracy of much of his conducting from memory. That his memory failed him at times, although rarely during his later years in England, was no more than a proof of his knowledge of the score ; had he been faking, as some averred, he would not have given himself away.

The system on which his memory worked was entirely individual, and cannot in any sense be regarded as learning the score. It is probable that the printed music meant little or nothing, and served merely as a reminder of previous impressions. One knows conductors like Leslie Heward, who, faced with the score of an unknown work, can sit down and read it at the piano, ignoring the many difficulties hidden in the lines of an orchestral score. Of others, like Toscanini, who have so exact a visual memory and so delicate an ear that the faintest divergence from the original is immediately discerned and placed. Beecham was capable of neither. His memory, I should say, is entirely aural. Once he has heard a work, the succession of notes and chords, however vague, remains fixed in his mind ; when the music begins again he can unfold the tale as if it were an impromptu. It was this impression of improvisation that gave most of his performances the freshness and vivid life which endeared him to sensitive audiences. The greatest example I witnessed of this extraordinary gift was when, at a Norwich Festival, he conducted the Delius *Mass of Life*, a work which, devoid of clear-cut form, would offer an almost insuperable problem to anyone who set himself to obtain a visual memorisation. Beecham's performance was monumental, not only as a feat of memory but as an achievement in devoted interpretation which would have been impossible had he relied for one moment on the printed score. Indeed, many singers, soloists and orchestral players will tell you of the fears which circulated on the rare occasions when Sir Thomas produced a score at a performance and carefully put on his spectacles ! But the *Mass of Life* was a re-creation.

This kind of aural memorisation has weaknesses which might prove fatal to the work of many musicians, but with Beecham it was the ideal method. For him, music is only to a slight degree an intellectual experience ; far more is it emotional, even physical, and once the performance begins he gives himself over to the music. But in doing so he avoids the obvious danger of a purely subjective enjoyment, which gives some conductors less right to lead the orchestra than to sit among the audience. It is as if Beecham becomes a vehicle for the music, so that in passing through him it elicits a lightning response which he is able to communicate no less rapidly to the players in front of him. In this way, the long lines of the music are made clear above all else, and even when mistakes occur they interfere so little with the main design that they are merely transitory, and frequently pass by the audience unremarked.

This spontaneous, intuitive approach to music, with its freedom and its minimum of technical justification, lays itself open to easy criticism, and Beecham's unorthodox manner of wielding the baton offers a *prise* to those who judge less by results than by methods. From this standpoint Sir Thomas can be easily condemned, and his highly individual gestures, *les moulinets de sir Beecham* as a distinguished French critic once described them to me, were often more perplexing to the audience than to the members of the orchestra. The listener, seeing nothing but the back of the conductor, missed many of the subtle facial expressions which conveyed so much of Beecham's message to the musicians under him. But, the few wiseacres apart, the ordinary concert-goer had no doubts that, notwithstanding the unorthodox methods used, this great little man gained an artistic result which few others could match. And even conductors who have been overshadowed by his prominence and his flair for publicity share the opinion of the public.

He owed his power over the orchestra, and, by them, over the audience, to his personality and to his uncanny knowledge of their psychology. Despite the annoyances and irritations to which his vagaries exposed the musicians who played for him, he never failed to gain his artistic ends when the time came. His method of rehearsal evoked severe criticism, for he often treated the most serious works in the most casual way ; but many of his rehearsals had little more in view than enabling him to hear certain passages once or twice, thus fixing them in his memory. He never made the mistake of reaching performance standard at rehearsal, and by this careful lack of preparation the players were kept on tiptoe, always a little fearful that the performance might go wrong. The nervous tension which resulted was the ideal state for Beecham to work his magic, getting effects which surprised the players directly responsible for them.

In the purely orchestral field he cannot be looked upon as an innovator ; the rôle he played was rather that of the refiner. For this he needed a responsive, highly efficient and sensitive instrument, and it was in his search for this, and in his finding it, that his greatest influence was felt. In this way, and, I think, in this way only, he belonged to his epoch, one which offered him the qualities he demanded. Had he been born here fifty years earlier, when the task of building an orchestral tradition from a collection of fragments had to be accomplished, he might well have turned his attentions to an equally brilliant if less perplexing occupation. The steady, undaunted persistence, the patience with second-rate material, and the slow but sure approach to the realisation of an ideal—in short, the pertinacity of a Sir Henry Wood—were outside his nature. Not that he liked things to be easy. A battle royal with someone or other, preferably one of the recognised musical institutions, was always a great stimulus, but it had to be a brilliant, noisy affair, with blades flashing even when blood did not flow.

His arrogance was a striking feature of his character, and although he rarely employed it against an isolated human being, except in the third person, when it was used as an excuse for cynical wit, it was the ideal weapon against any institution which, in his opinion, buttressed the wall of Philistinism he was attacking. Beecham, here at his most quixotic, found no lack of windmills to tilt at. But finding all tilting in vain, he pretended to ignore the windmills and, with a magnificent gesture, while his active brain was scheming and planning, he formed his own orchestra. Now, he must have thought, I am free. Now I can show the world that in the whole of England there is at least one man whose gifts, tasks and standards will save the country from the artistic damnation it deserves. And many of those who heard the London Philharmonic Orchestra for the first time in October 1932, when it appeared almost overnight with the fine flower of the orchestral profession in its ranks, would have agreed that here at last was an organisation with all the essential qualities. A genius, even if a wayward one, for its conductor ; a hand-picked personnel ; solid financial backing, with the scares of 1929 safely past, and a triumphantly favourable Press. Only one thing was wrong, and that at first was not easily discernible. Beecham was *not* free. Some thirty years of battling with prejudice had given him what might be termed an 'institution' complex. Every problem was seen from the point of view of the original artist ; every opportunity of showing England and the world what he and his orchestra could achieve was grasped at ; every chance of displaying the worth of certain music and composers was taken. For the conductor who was an artist, and no more, no higher aims could be desired, and had the matter rested there the glory that was the pre-war L.P.O. would have remained undimmed. But the matter could not rest there. This outlook, in one who was solely responsible for co-ordinating the artistic and economic existence of such a highly organised activity as a symphony orchestra, ended in anarchy. Had he been a German prince, or an obsessed King Ludwig of Bavaria, with all the power and resources he needed for his task, he could have made and consolidated musical history in England. For that he was born too late, as for a full realisation of the social meaning of music he was born too soon.

When the London Philharmonic Orchestra was first formed

Sir Thomas was artistic director, a sufficiently onerous task even while the right conditions were present, and while the financial side looked after itself. Throughout his life he had insisted on an artistic integrity according to his lights, and had spent untold sums of money to preserve it. In the early thirties he was no less insistent, but who was to foot the bill? Obviously, in a healthy country the work he had already done, crowned by the founding of the L.P.O., this 'collection of thoroughbreds,' would have earned him the recognition he needed, even while he disdained to plead for it. Despairing of this, he continued to move within his own circle, with a lynx-like eye for anyone willing to subsidise his splendid, grandiose schemes, watching for every tendency likely to further his very clear ideals. Unfortunate in his choice of colleagues and satellites, incapable of selecting and retaining anything like an ideal staff, he found himself saddled not only with as much work as any conductor could honestly hope to carry through, but with a load of organisational responsibility which, despite his gifts, was beyond his power. His unreliability, his irregularity, his inconstancy and the inequality of his artistic achievements came from all this. In his high disdain of Philistinism he failed to see that some of those from whom he sought help were themselves the arch-Philistines, whose superficial respect for art was a veneer for cynical disregard of it. What was more, in his hatred for moribund British traditions he included a contempt for what to him was one more institution, the public. In many of his speeches he pointed a scornful finger at its weaknesses, its prejudices and its lack of appreciation of all that he was offering it. Never did he take it into his confidence. To him this public was static, like all the institutions he knew. Never did he realise that a public was ready, waiting to be led along the golden path of music. Conscious of his power to move an audience, he never dreamed that he might have become the leader of a public in movement. And so he continued to cast his pearls.

MY LAST TWO MEMORIES of Sir Thomas Beecham are the most vivid of any. There was the final concert which he conducted in this country before leaving for Australia on a tour which took him at length to the United States. The programme was entirely devoted to the music of Sibelius, for the concert had a charitable connection with the country which, at that epoch, was known as 'poor little Finland.' I had ceased playing in the London Philharmonic Orchestra a few weeks previously, and for part of this performance stood in the highest balcony of Queen's Hall, where now only the music of the wind is heard, looking down on the concentrated, single-visioned audience which watched and listened spellbound. I have since regretted that I should have been little more than an onlooker on that occasion, which Beecham's prolonged absence from England has made historic. Even without this added significance it was a great occasion, and the audience, roused by their knowledge that this most spectacular figure was appearing for the last time, at a period when any leave-taking might become permanent, reacted to the music in such a way that a great performance was inevitable. *Tapiola*, that masterpiece of emotional intensity, burned like fire.

After the concert the members of the orchestra gave a supper party to Sir Thomas, as if to clinch the new understanding which had grown up during the first six months of the war. Sir Thomas arrived as soon as he was able to escape from Queen's Hall, where he had, indeed, given his final performance. The party was held in an upper room at Pagani's Restaurant, of which now only a bare façade and one room remain ; Fate has broken two of the threads which linked the orchestra and its former conductor. Until the moment arrived for the inevitable speech he was as quiet and reserved as the most unimportant guest, with none of the display of feeling or temperament which might have been expected from an artist who had come from one of his most resounding successes, and who was destined to leave the scene of a long career almost at once. His speech, however, gave expression to all this. Beginning, in the usual manner of his impromptus, with a few witticisms to cover commonplaces, he developed his theme of the English inability to appreciate officially the real values of life, and built up a damning argument against our traditional blindness to the meaning of culture. Despite the wit and fooling which, as in Shaw, have often tended to obscure the subtle point he was making, there was an earnestness and a bitterness which had been more difficult to detect in many of his other speeches, with their perversities and paradox.

The wit of his speeches, and this was often looked for when it was not present, has done much damage to Beecham. The conquests of his baton were often thrown away by his tongue, so that he could come to be described by one of our leading musicians as a 'garrulous old gentleman who had once conducted.' This was as unjust and superficial as the applause of those who laughed as soon as he made any remark at all, as a crowd will laugh at a famous comedian before he has made his first joke. But the points he intended to bring out were rarely the obvious ones. When, in return for the hospitality received at the hands of the Berlin Philharmonic Orchestra in 1936, we invited them to a dinner at the Savoy Hotel during a tour they were making in England, Beecham gave a speech. In the course of it he said, 'While we were in Germany I made thirty-nine speeches, the same number as the articles of the English Church, and every one of them was different. In reply to my orations, a high German official of one designation or another made a similar number of speeches, each of which was identical, thus showing the superiority of the Teutonic mind.' The Germans appeared satisfied, and the deadly wisecrack on the sterility of Fascism passed almost unnoticed. But on the occasion of the farewell supper party, when he was among the group of musicians with whom he had worked so long, he ceased to play up to his reputation as a popular jester, and the full realisation of the artistic tragedy was apparent.

I recently read a report in an American newspaper which spoke of Sir Thomas as one of those 'whom the war had washed up on the shores of the United States.' To accept this is not only to do a grave injustice to Beecham : it is to make it impossible to assess his position in the society of his time, or to understand the significance of his departure. His plans to leave England had been made months before the war broke out, and his decision not to conduct the L.P.O. for a considerable period—a decision he renounced for the benefit of musicians on the outbreak of war —was announced in the Press early in 1939.

It is difficult to resist the symbolism of the broken threads I have mentioned above ; the war-time destruction of the Queen's Hall, of a restaurant famous for its musical and artistic associations, and the breaking of a tradition in the exile of Sir Thomas Beecham. Perhaps it is more than symbolism. Perhaps these sad events were no more than a series of effects due to common causes. A consistent lack of foresight during the period 1918 to 1939, that coming-of-age of wanton stupidity, with its careless disregard of values, and its entire lack of faith in the only final standard—human nature ; these were the qualities responsible for the three losses, and for many more. The material things, concert-halls and restaurants, can be rebuilt, and the tradition begun by Sir Thomas has been revolutionised, but maintained on a different level and with a wider scope. Under the stress of war, the London Philharmonic Orchestra has mastered a lesson which its founder failed to learn ; that only the support of the great public can be relied upon. When Sir Thomas returns to conduct the Orchestra of his creation, believing in the new response the war has awakened, the wheel will have turned full circle, and history have been irrevocably made.

PAUL NASH

ERIC NEWTON

The particular Englishness of English art is something that, as far as I know, has never been successfully analysed by any critic or art historian. True, the outward signs by which it can be recognised have often been pointed out—the love of line, the decorative inventiveness, the firm draughtsmanship, the obsession with detail, the timidity of colour, the hatred of the grand manner, the lack of painterliness. But these are not qualities of mind or temperament : they are merely the symptoms of such qualities. They are effects, not causes. And yet there is a type of art so deep-rootedly English that none but an Englishman can understand it.

I have seen Frenchmen whose judgment I respect stand baffled in front of what seemed to me manifest, if minor, works of genius. They were too English. They could not be explained by French standards. They were enigmas. Therefore (such is French logic) they were negligible.

I do not apologise for prefacing an account of Paul Nash's painting with a paragraph pointing out that the Englishness of English painting is a very definite but a rather elusive thing. Paul Nash's name is one of twenty that spring to my mind whenever I try to isolate this particular quality. They could never have come from any country but England, these twenty, and it is only because, in the years before the war, so many of us were hypnotised by propaganda radiating from Paris, that their uniqueness was not praised. My list of twenty includes some famous names, but other names, equally famous, have no place in it. It includes Hogarth and Blake and Turner, but Reynolds is not on it, nor even Gainsborough and certainly not Constable. Despite the aggressive affection for England that is Constable's keynote, his landscapes are not the outcome of an English way of seeing or feeling. Madox Brown is high up on my list : so is Stanley Spencer. Calvert, Samuel Palmer, the young Millais, Eric Ravilious, Graham Sutherland, yes. Watts, Sargent, Whistler, Sickert, Augustus John, Matthew Smith, no.

Does that look as though I had picked my own favourites and labelled them 'genuine home-grown' in order to prove that my own æsthetic bias has a sound patriotic foundation ? Nothing of the kind, I assure you. I consider Watts a shamefully underrated artist, I am entranced by Sickert's painterliness, Matthew Smith, at his best, can make his neighbours on the walls of any contemporary British exhibition look overwrought and tired. But I maintain that other countries could have produced them, or something like them. Yes, of course I admit that Sickert is squarer, less muscular than Degas, that Watts is more priggish than Titian, that Matthew Smith lacks the *chic* of Matisse and the passion of Soutine. They have a veneer that brands them as English but the foundation that holds the veneer in place comes from elsewhere.

SOON AFTER THE outbreak of the present war it was decided that a set of records of its many phases should be made by

K

artists. Good academic artists were available in abundance, and some of them were entrusted with the work. There were other artists who had never been academic, who had always been quite unrepentantly personal, and some of these were also entrusted with the work. Paul Nash was among them. It turned out, as any but the most timid might have foreseen, that the competent, academic artists had very little to say about the war, while the aloof, the difficult artists revealed an unexpected power to comment on the tension, the fantasy and the tragedy of it. That was partly because their tasks were allotted to them with unusual intelligence (if Henry Moore had been told to draw aeroplanes and Stanley Spencer the perils of convoy work in the Atlantic both would have made a mess of it), but more important was the fact of their Englishness. Matisse, Marie Laurencin and Dufy, whatever they had been told to do, would have made a much worse mess of it. They would not have known where to begin. Paul Nash had made mordant comments on the last war through the medium of landscape. This time his job was to paint aeroplanes. In order to realise what made the choice almost inevitable it will be necessary to begin at the beginning.

Behind every work of visual art there are two motive forces—a love of (and therefore an exceptional understanding of) the thing depicted : and a love of (and therefore an exceptional mastery over) the elements in the work of art itself. The two are by no means mutually exclusive. In fact, some kind of fusion of the two is necessary before the work of art can come into being, though the proportions in which they co-exist in any given work vary. In the greatest art they are more or less equal and the fusion is complete. In contemporary French art the object depicted counts for much less in its own right than as a starting-point for the solution of a set of purely æsthetic problems. In English painting (and herein, I think, lie the strength and the weakness of English art) the love of the object for its own sake predominates. To over-simplify this statement by saying that English art tends to be literary or descriptive is to confuse the issue. The painter's job is visual. It consists in communicating an adventure of the artist's eye to the eye of the spectator, thereby giving him (the spectator) a new capacity for visual adventure. The artist who is merely literary or merely descriptive has no capacity for visual adventure. But adventure, visual or other,

PLATE 1: COAST SCENE (1920)

PLATE 2: LANDSCAPE OF THE MONOLITHS (1938)

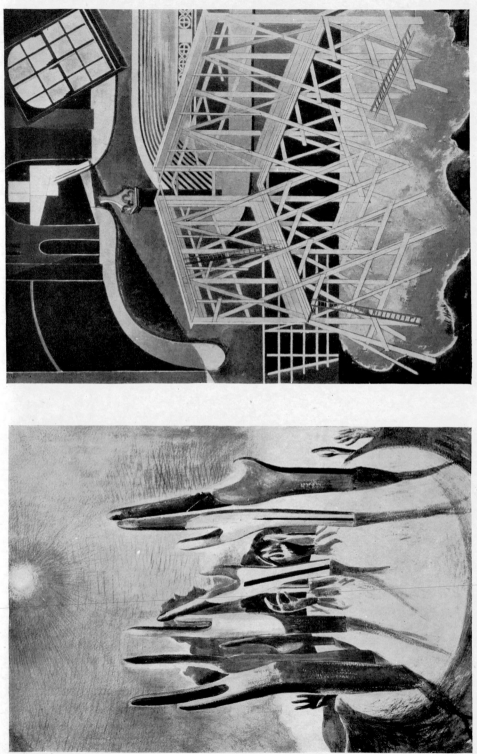

PLATE 4: NORTHERN ADVENTURE (1928)

PLATE 3: WOOD ON THE HILL (1937)

can come either from within or from without. The artist can paint either with his eye on the world about him (the English way) or with his eye on his canvas (the French way). In either case it is the quality of his vision that explains his genius or lack of it. Paul Nash, like Frith, and like all truly English painters, paints with his eye on the world about him ; but Paul Nash can extract more meaning out of a piece of flint than Frith could out of a crowded railway station. The flint has been seen with an abnormally sensitive eye, the crowd at the station merely with the eye of a normally observant man.

So it is not only the direction but the quality of this visual sensitiveness that calls for analysis. In Paul Nash's case both are well worth analysing.

Its direction has varied considerably from time to time, taking strange leaps and then pausing to digest, heading off at unexpected tangents but always retaining something of previous adventures whenever it has tackled a new theme.

The quality of it, on the other hand, has changed more slowly and as it changed one can follow a slow but logical development of style.

First, then, what *kinds* of things has Paul Nash loved ? (Loved is the only appropriate word in this connection. Only a passionate and affectionate interest in the thing seen will explain the intensity of the thing painted.) Glancing through a chronologically arranged series of his paintings, what strikes one first is the increasing narrowness and concentration of his vision. Whatever he selects, it is usually an isolated thing—the curl of a breaking wave, the compact, complex surface of a stone or a pair of stones, the roughness of a tree's root or the sharp edge of a broken sheet of metal. True, in 1917, when Nash was first caught up by the immense implications of the last war, his horizon widened, as it was bound to. There was so much that was clamouring to be seen, so many avenues open to visual adventure, that his work attained, momentarily, a greater complexity than was natural to him. 'Void' (1917) (Plate 10) is probably his most elaborately organised picture. For once he has refused to focus with his usual narrow-angle lens on one object or kind of object. Knowing his limitations, one would have expected the picture to lack cohesion. But it does cohere, and not merely because it is held together by a consistent mood. Rain, shell bursts, chaos, destruction, and an extraordinary accumulation of objects, each one seen and recorded with the integrity of a conscientious eye-witness, are welded together into a satisfactory whole by a set of angular lines that drive their way diagonally across and through the picture. For a man of twenty-five it is an unusually good example of how to contain the parts within the whole, and until quite recently Nash never came nearer to fusing formal design with visual experience, neither sacrificed to the other, the one acting as a vessel to contain the other. The picture has not the intensity of much of his later work, but it has a bigger sweep which can easily be accounted for by the unusual emotional pressure from without. The same increase in emotional pressure was to occur again in 1941, and with very much the same kind of result.

Once this temporary pressure had eased, as it was bound to, Nash began to explore his own particular world in his own way. He could set his own pace and choose his own fields of research. Landscape—the bowery English scene, simplified but not yet concentrated—had been his subject before the war. In 1917 he continued to use it but with a special twist, as though he welcomed with relief the unboweriness of shattered tree stumps. And again, since the war, the English scene absorbed him for a number of years. Yet I cannot think of him as a landscape painter in the usual sense. He can turn a landscape into the appropriate and even the inevitable setting for a portrait—always a portrait of a *thing*, and never of a *person*. And, in the light of his later work, whenever he paints pure landscape I have the impression that here is the perfect setting for a portrait of some object which has unaccountably disappeared, leaving the picture interesting but incomplete, a stage empty of actors.

But there is no such sense of incompleteness about his pictures of the sea and the sea-wall at Dymchurch, severely simplified statements of the structure of waves and jetties, that date from 1920 onwards (Plate 1). Here he is more in his element. No boweriness, no lush sentiment to be pruned away. The sea provides its own drama. It has no need of actors. Its very emptiness is part of the meaning of these pictures. Then comes a series of paintings which begin by exploring the possibilities of views through windows, the contrast between the confined and the unconfined, and end by feeling their way outwards into pure space. All kinds of devices are used to make this sense of space vivid, slender scaffolding that leads the eye into remote interplanetary distances or receding spheres threading their way through the scaffolding (Plate 6). Then comes a growing obsession with stones, their shapes and surfaces, their odd complexity, their relationship with their environment, an obsession that began with a visit to Avebury (Plate 2). This again develops and spreads. The stones themselves begin to acquire a personality, so that from being merely studies of surface and structure the pictures begin to have curious psychological implications. And then the interest spread from stones to all kinds of earth-bound things, tree-stumps, stone walls, even a set of glove-stretchers whose odd gesticulations start in Nash a new imaginative urge, so that he sees them rooted in the ground on a bare hill-top (Plate 3).

Then, just before the present war, comes a period in which he seems to gather together the fruits of these researches and fuse them into bigger units. 'Monster Shore' (Plate 12) is typical of this phase. It contains all the elements that he has been exploring —the wave forms, the tree forms, the stony textures, and the sense of space inviting the eye to explore the picture in depth.

The outbreak of war again began to produce an enlargement, a quickening of the emotional tempo, but not at once. Just as 'Void' and the 'Menin Road' were not painted till the third year of the last war, so 'Totes Meer' (Plate 8) and the 'Battle of Britain' are reflections of a set of experiences that were gradual and cumulative. Before such pictures could be painted a good deal of preparation was necessary.

'Preparation,' in any artist's work, can be of two kinds. He may either make a series of isolated studies to be incorporated later, without much alteration, in a larger work ; or he may regard his preliminary drawings as a means of working his way gradually under the skin of his subject. This is Nash's method in 'Totes Meer.' For example, the rather untidy, formless water-colour of a wrecked enemy aeroplane (Plate 9) seems at first sight to have no direct connection with 'Totes Meer,' and yet it has a connection. It is a kind of thinking aloud about the nature of twisted and torn metal surfaces, a piece of research not necessarily incorporated into the picture, but none the less a contribution to it.

Preparation of the other kind, the collection of documentary detail, Nash has found he can safely entrust to the camera. It is a dangerous method and it can only be used by an eye that has already collected and stored up an immense fund of visual experience. Sickert could use the camera as a crutch to lean on, but only at the end of a long life of patient observation. Nash takes his own photographs and uses them partly to ensure documentary accuracy in detail and partly to reinforce his visual memory of an unusually complex set of objects.

'Totes Meer,' then, like 'Void,' is a synthesis of research and observation, but the fusion of the two is more complete, for now he has another twenty-five years of experience to draw on. Those early studies of long lines of breakers hammering impotently at the sea-wall of Dymchurch have given him the power to sort out and organise the wreckage of German planes into frozen, impotent breakers hammering at the defences of Britain. His early studies of pure space have enabled him to place that dump of wreckage in an illimitable landscape ; his studies of textures, to give it a prickly tangibility that makes one's finger-tips tingle. 'The Battle of Britain,' a later picture in the same series, tackles a more difficult problem—the problem of how to represent pictorially the fleets of opposing planes grappling in the upper air while England lies spread out like a map below, awaiting the outcome of the struggle.

But these two canvases are not his only war pictures. Aeroplanes in general have been his set theme, and here again he has been able to turn to good account his, by this time, uncanny mastery of space. His studies of static scaffolding poised in space have now become studies of dynamic scaffolding moving through space. But his aeroplanes are more than mere mechanical shapes. Just as his stones and trees began to develop a dramatic personality of their own, so his aeroplanes have developed their own personality—not merely the personality common to all planes, but each type of plane begins to become an individual, a particular kind of dragon or monster. A Hampden bomber (Plate 5), making its urgent way through and above moonlit clouds, is not just any bomber. It is, to quote his own words, 'perhaps the strangest of them all. . . . It is rather clumsy. And, in heaven's name ! what does it look like ? No fish, not a bird, not quite a reptile, not wholly an insect. Yet all these negatives suggest a

PLATE 5: MOONLIGHT VOYAGE: HAMPDEN FLYING
ABOVE THE CLOUDS (1940)

PLATE 6: VOYAGES OF THE MOON (1934-37)

PLATE 7: PHOTOGRAPH—WRECKED GERMAN PLANES

PLATE 8: TOTES MEER (1941)

positive. We can only find the equivalent of the Hampden Bomber in the mists of pre-history. It is plainly some sort of pterodactyl. It has something of the reptile and yet—apart from being a plane—it is a creature of the skies. . . . It sets out across the darkling fields soaring into the dusk with its great satanic nose sniffing the upper air. Presently the moon rises and there goes the flying lizard, gliding across the cloud edge, its pale eyes flickering in the lunar ray. Flying against Germany.'

Again, it is typically English, this obsession with the object. One's first discovery about Paul Nash is the easy discovery that he is a painter-poet, an artist to whom it is the mood that matters : and that, like all poets, he will sacrifice the fact to the mood, distort the fact to intensify the mood—an unreliable person when it comes to making records of shapes, not a man to be trusted by technical experts thinking in terms of dihedral angles and aspect ratios. One's second discovery about him is that he is, after all, a recorder : that his shapes are more accurate than one had supposed : that, oddly enough, though his paintings have none of the superficial mannerisms of the photograph they are essentially photographic. One's final discovery is the important realisation that the world of his mind's eye actually owes its haunting, dreamlike quality to the precision of his physical eye. Having been excited by what a piece of flint, an uprooted tree, a view through a window looks like, he weaves his spells out of their *look*, not out of their *feel*. One of Blake's marginalia to Reynolds's Discourses runs, 'The difference between a bad Artist and a Good One is : the Bad Artist seems to copy a great deal. The Good one Really does Copy a Great Deal.' Or listen to J. M. Synge on the same theme : 'When I was writing *The Shadow of the Glen* I got more aid than any learning could have given me from a chink in that floor of the old Wicklow house where I was staying, that let me hear what was being said by the servant girls in the kitchen.' To what extent Paul Nash 'copies' can be fairly gauged by a comparison between a photograph taken by the artist himself, of a dump of wrecked German planes (Plate 7), and his 'Totes Meer.' It is difficult to decide which is more remarkable, the resemblance between the photograph and the painting or the difference between them. It is only when one adds to them the third element, the water-colour sketch, that one sees what has happened. The camera has been used as a kind of third eye, to confirm the artist's intention, to search out, on the spot, the wavelike forms already visualised in his imagination, and to record their actual appearance. It has been called in, as it were, to supply corroborative and detailed evidence about something that the artist had already apprehended intuitively. Nothing much has been altered. The wheel, the smooth surfaces, the torn edges, the glimpses of metal skeletons under the surface, all are there in both. But the process that has turned the record of a phenomenon into the record of an experience is revealed by the sketch. It enables one to eavesdrop into the creative process. It is a kind of halfway house between the bunch of grapes and the bottle of brandy, almost a blue-print of the distillery. The harsh edges, the sense of visual discomfort they arouse (as though the retina of the eye were being torn by the spiky chaos it contemplates), is isolated and extracted, so that none of its flavour shall be lost in the final product ; so that the final product can even afford a certain amount of grace and suavity because the flavour is certain to be predominant in it. The hint of breakers is there in the photograph for those who have eyes to see it. In the picture it becomes a positive theme that the eye cannot miss. But fused with the rhythmic Dymchurch waves is the metallic prickliness of the sketch. The idea of turning metal into a sea is purely poetical—a kind of metaphor in paint. The painting of the waves is visual. The fusion of the two results in that particular kind of visual poetry that I am trying to account for.

Equally remarkable is the use made of a photograph (Plate 11) in 'Monster Shore.' The uprooted tree is certainly striking even in a photograph, though I doubt if one would be arrested by it if it were not that Nash has by this time accustomed our eyes to the harsh beauty of such objects. But its use, again almost without alteration, as an element in the picture is another instance of how the creative artist works. In the photograph the tree is no more than an interesting example of shape and texture. In the picture it becomes the central character in a drama acted by inanimate objects. (Paul Nash's art might be summed up as an exploration of the dramatic possibilities of inanimate objects.) 'Monster Shore' is as good a laboratory specimen as one could find for the purpose of analysing Nash's particular brand of poetic record.

PLATE 9: WRECKAGE (1941)

PLATE 10: VOID (1917)

PLATE 11: UPROOTED TREE (PHOTOGRAPH)

PLATE 12: MONSTER SHORE (1939)

Surrealism, of course, contributes. Or it would be more accurate to say that Nash has that heightened sense of how commonplace objects can acquire new significance merely through juxtaposition, which is one of the foundation stones of Surrealism. That absurdly formal platform, with two doorsteps which evidently belong to a Notting Hill[1] residence, is not in itself remarkable. But place it on the edge of a swift stream and it becomes sinister as well as absurd. Place on the other side of the stream the gnarled and uprooted monster of the photograph, like a sentry lying in wait for the traveller who dares to take off from the excessively urban doorstep. Lead—no, drag—the eye across the river by that sequence of three tree-stumps, and then lead it still further up a low cliff to a range of hills and you have the appropriate setting for a drama that has nothing to do with æsthetics. You start off on a purely psychological adventure in which you and the formal respectability of the doorstep and the uncouthness of the tree gaze at each other uncomprehendingly.

As your mind jumps backwards and forwards from the step to the tree it becomes conscious of a quality that pervades all Nash's later pictures. Pausing to wonder why everything he paints seems to give out the same kind of note, I have often searched my mind for the exact word to describe this particular mood. And often the word 'arid' has risen to the surface, sometimes to be accepted as the *exactly* right word, sometimes to be rejected as nearly right but unjust because of the implied sense of disparagement. Dryness is certainly almost always there, but it is not the dryness of drought. It is the dryness of the moon. The kernel of it is a dry, moon-haunted nostalgia that rules out the possibility of springtime, of rising sap or lush grass or laughter. His world is always uninhabited. Organic life is banished from it, yet the inorganic objects that pervade it are possessed of a strange vitality of their own.

Look at 'Northern Adventure' (Plate 4). The scaffolding in the street below has an expectant air, the broad flight of steps leading to St Pancras Station is charged with electricity, the neo-Gothic gateway seems to point, the curve of the pavement seems to beckon, the window (isolated from its architectural context) seems to be craning sideways and peering into the fateful gateway to the station. Everything in the picture is

---

[1] The artist tells me that he found them in the middle of a field near Swanage.

natural, credible, even banal. Only the juxtapositions make it a setting for adventure.

This rarefied, expectant mood is a thing that only a creative mind could evoke. It is by no means pure Surrealism, but it owes its existence to a realisation of something that the Surrealists have made it their business to cultivate assiduously—far too assiduously. Paul Nash gravitates naturally towards the dream-drama. But he is not content to manufacture a synthetic dream out of his own inner consciousness. The dream-world comes to him in the form of a direct visual experience. An uprooted tree, a smashed aeroplane, a shell-shattered battlefield, the moon travelling through space, St Pancras Station, these are phenomena whose meaning varies with the eye that beholds them. Why is it that Blake, using precisely the same ingredients as Flaxman, can create a world so much richer in content ? It is not true that he achieves a new meaning by distorting or exaggerating familiar shapes. Like Nash, Blake distorts more rarely and less violently than is commonly supposed. Like Nash, Blake (perhaps this is one of the chief secrets of their kinship) 'does copy a great deal.' If the strange power that certain artists possess of making magic out of everyday things could be analysed and explained, art criticism would be a more serviceable and a more entertaining form of literature. As it is, the critic must leave off just where the fun begins. Or else he must turn artist himself and try for a magic of words, a kind of second-hand magic, that runs roughly parallel to the visual magic that has started him off. Failing that, he can only write of the artist's methods, and assume that their results will be apprehended intuitively. He can only say, for example, that Nash weaves his spells of the same stuff that the Surrealists use, but that he uses a very different method and achieves a very different result.

Most Surrealists start with a determination to produce something awfully significant, and then search for objects that will serve their purpose. Paul Nash looks squarely at the world (admittedly the inanimate world) and then says to himself 'That's significant : I'll paint it.'

It is a sounder way of going to work. Masterpieces are not born of a will to produce masterpieces but of a desire to externalise and pass on to others something that has happened to oneself.

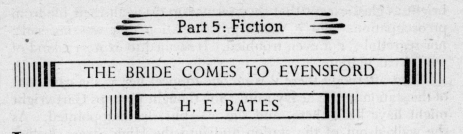

THE BRIDE COMES TO EVENSFORD

H. E. BATES

It was thirty-one years since she had first come up by the one-track railway to Evensford, where from, only two people knew : a girl of twenty-three, carrying all her belongings in a new straw dress-basket, on a wet April afternoon when flocks of pearl-grey sea-gulls floated in the spring floods by the river and clear rain shone steel-grey on the unpainted domes of the new gaso-meters of the station. Then, as it still did, the three-coach train came in backwards, engine behind. It ran up from the junction past the iron furnaces, across the fourteen brick arches of the track over the river, past the wooden signal-box where the key of the branch-line was surrendered and then retrieved by the fireman on the return journey, past the brick-works and the factories, and so under the yellow footbridge to where on the platform carrier pigeons muttered softly in flat baskets as they waited for the returning train. In thirty-one years it was surprising how little these things had changed. Nor was there much change in Evensford itself. To her it still seemed, except for herself and one other person, a town of the dead.

She had come to Evensford that day to be head assistant in the drapery shop of Fred Cartwright, Manchester and London warehouse. Cartwright had known her for about two years as Miss Cassell, head of the blouse department of a Macclesfield warehouse in Cannon Street, where he went to buy on the first Monday of every month. The Miss Cassell whom Fred Cartwright knew was a tall girl with light brown hair and delicate, efficient hands. She was not particularly good-looking, but Cartwright liked her. Her neck seemed rather too long, but she wore round it a band of black velvet that gave her a sort of stateliness. Apart from her lovely hands—she could play the piano very well—the most striking thing about her was her eyes. They were very curious, though Cartwright never seemed to notice that. They were a cold clear grey and they would have been as shallow and bright as glass except that they seemed to draw all their life from preoccupation. But it was a preoccupation that was not sad ; nor regretful ; nor even troubled. It seemed to express a kind of wistful calculation.

That afternoon there was no one to meet her as she came out of the station in the heavy rain. She thought perhaps Cartwright might have been there, and she was bitterly disappointed. As she walked out of the station and into the High Street, feeling very alone and friendless, she lifted her face to the rain and had her first sight of Evensford. Any moment of the future when Evensford seemed like a town of the dead was half a repetition of that moment. The emptiness of the street made her stop abruptly on the pavement. The rain beat on her face and clothes and hands, but she did not seem to notice it. It was early closing day and the blinds of the shops were down and there was no traffic moving. The slates of the roofs were iron-grey in the rain and the street was iron-grey too except for patches of horse-manure washed into tobacco-yellow pools by the rain and rainbow patches of orange-skin oil streaming down the camber of the road and flowing down the brown water of the gutters. As she walked up the street, feeling the handle of the dress-basket grow stickier under the rain, she looked at the shops. Here and there a blind was not drawn and she could see in a window a few boxes of fly-blown confectionery, rolls of cheap lino, a pile of dirty cabbages pressed against the glass, a group of clumsy, fusty dummies wearing last year's styles. And in the windows where blinds were drawn she could see the reflection of herself, tall, slim-waisted, rather stately, rather aloof, skimming smoothly past. One or two people passed her as she walked farther up the deserted street, but whenever they looked at her she lifted her head and looked at the names on the shop-fronts, her face deliberately upturned. 'So this,' she thought, 'is Evensford. This is it,' as if she had clearly made up her mind never to be part of it all.

When she got to the Cartwright shop, a double-windowed place with black strip shutters and a small gallery with a flagpole outside the windows upstairs, she rang the bell of the private door in the side alley-way. But it was not Cartwright who answered her, and again she was disappointed.

'I am Mrs Cartwright,' the woman said. 'Mr Cartwright's mother.'

'Oh yes,' she said. 'I am Miss Cassell.'

'Miss Cassell from London?'

'Yes.'

'But we thought it was Saturday.'

'No, it was Thursday. Mr Cartwright said distinctly Thursday. I've got the letter. It was distinctly Thursday.'

'How ridiculous. How stupid.'

'I'm sorry.'

'Oh, no! Not you, not you. Not you at all. Fred, Mr Cartwright. Just like him. No sense of reality at all. He just floats from day to day. One day just like another. Anyway, come in out of the rain, Miss Cassell, come in.'

Mrs Cartwright was dressed in black with many pins stuck into the bodice of her dress. Her face was angular and thin and white, with brown eyes that were dark underneath. As she stepped back into the house she seemed to dissolve into the darkness of the passage, so that only the pale face and the pale hands and the little silver pins remained distinctly visible. Miss Cassell followed her into the passage and set the wet dress-basket on the floor. Mrs Cartwright picked it up. It was a gesture of suave annoyance. It made Miss Cassell so blank and impotent with resentment that she could not speak or move. 'I'll take it into the kitchen,' Mrs Cartwright said. 'Then I'll show you upstairs.'

They went upstairs, neither she nor Mrs Cartwright speaking. The house had a clean, barren smell, almost a holy smell, of cleanliness. It came down the dark pine stairs like a cool draught and it hung in the bedroom, about the white wooden chest-of-drawers and the small brass bedstead and the ivy-flowered shining lino and over the plush-framed texts on the walls, like a sterilising invisible cloud.

'This is the room we thought of giving you until you can find lodgings,' Mrs Cartwright said.

'Thank you.'

'You will excuse me now. I'm doing the books. I always do the books on Thursday afternoon.'

'Yes. Is Mr Cartwright in?'

'Mr Cartwright is asleep. He generally sleeps on Thursday afternoons.'

'Could I have my dress-basket? My things?'

'It was very wet,' Mrs Cartwright said. 'The girl will bring it up.'

Later it took her more than an hour, moving slowly, to unpack and change her things. Her coat and hat and stockings were very wet, and she hung them on the bedrail to dry until she could take them downstairs. The house was completely silent : as if Cartwright and his mother, and even the maid, had forgotten her. As she dressed she looked down on the wet street below. It was from her window that you reached the little balcony. She stood for a long time watching the rain dripping from the empty flag-pole down on to the empty street, not realising how often she would stand there and watch the rain dripping in that same way, and then finally when she was dressed and ready she went downstairs.

It was a strange reception, but it became stranger still. Downstairs she stood in the dark hall and listened for a sound of life. Somewhere the rain was dribbling with a choking sound from a gutter, and it was the only sound she could hear for some time. The passage was long and narrow, with two doors on either side and a single door at the opposite end from the entrance. She opened one of the side doors and looked in. It was the dining-room and tea was laid at a round mahogany table, but the room was empty. She shut the door and stood rather apprehensively listening again : not nervous, only rather proud and lonely and injured. Then before she could open another door, and while she was still wondering about Cartwright and his mother, she heard a sound. It came from the door at the end of the passage : a soft irregular sound rather like the sound of a gently bouncing ball.

She opened the door, and it was the shop itself, dark now except for a little light coming in at the unshuttered side-window, and the sound was the sound of a white cat playing along the counter with an unravelled roll of dark red ribbon. She took the cat in her arms and stroked it and walked slowly round the shop with it in her hands. As she looked up at the shelves of materials, the print, the satin and the calico, the hat-boxes, the ribbons, the ranges of drawers all neatly lettered, the flat rolls of fabrics and blankets piled against the walls, she looked something like a cat herself, very quiet, rather deliberate, her eyes full of sleepy concentration. She was to know later that Cartwright's was the largest shop of its kind in Evensford ; but the knowledge did not tell her any more than her walk round the shop on that first wet April afternoon with the white cat in her hands : the cat that was to be almost her only friend in Evensford for quite some years. The shop, fusty and dark, a little old-fashioned but sound and prosperous, satisfied and comforted and even excited one part of herself. The cat thrust its cool wet nose against her long throat and comforted and excited another.

Coming out of the shop, still carrying the cat in her hands, she was in time to see Mrs Cartwright emerging from another door. The long angular face looked rather grim and spare.

'I couldn't find my way,' Miss Cassell said. 'I opened the wrong door and found the cat playing with the ribbons.'

'All right,' Mrs Cartwright said. 'In future *this* is the drawing-room, *that* is my office, and *this* is the dining room. I daresay tea will be ready now, Miss Cassell,' she said. 'Fred !'

There emerged almost immediately, from the drawing-room, the figure of Cartwright himself. He was sleepily smoothing his thin dark hair with his hands. He did not seem to Miss Cassell at all like the Mr Cartwright she knew : the well-brushed, easy-talking, persuasive Mr Cartwright who in London gave the feeling of self-reliance and prosperity and took her to lunch at somewhere a little above the usual A B C and rode with her on the tops of buses with his hat on his knees, laughing rather too heartily, and bought her buttonholes of red roses and maidenhair on early spring afternoons. There was no sign of this Mr Cartwright, who seemed to have been replaced by someone who had suddenly been cruelly awakened and was trying to decide what day and what time of day it was.

'Fred, if you've had your sleep out,' Mrs Cartwright said, 'this is Miss Cassell. And why did you say Thursday if you meant Saturday ?'

'I think—I——'

'Sometimes I think you'll never grow up,' Mrs Cartwright said. 'Sometimes I think you'll never grow up.'

'I'm sorry, mother. I'm sorry, Miss——'

'I should think so. I should indeed think you are sorry. Now say good afternoon to Miss Cassell in a proper manner.'

'Good afternoon, Miss Cassell,' Cartwright said.

'Good afternoon,' she said.

'I'm sorry I——'

'Let us have tea now,' his mother said, 'let us have tea. And put the cat down, Miss Cassell, please.'

At tea the girl sat very silent, listening and watching. It was as if Cartwright, a man of twenty-eight or nine, were a small boy. 'Your tea is already sugared, Fred. Don't be so absent-minded. Pay attention!' It was as if he had never made, and had no means of making, an independent personal decision about his life. 'Some more bread and butter, Fred! Take another slice. Go on! You don't eat enough!'

It surprised her very much that Cartwright should be so meek. In London he had sometimes given her the impression of a man of rosy enterprise. There was a dream or two of which he had sometimes given her a glimpse as they rode home to her lodgings on the bus-top. They were dreams of the shop. From these dreams she already knew something of what the turnover of the shop was, how it had decreased or stood still, how Cartwright planned to increase it. She was attracted by these figures, by the possibility of the dreams, as another woman might have been attracted by the dream of marriage. They were in fact her dream of marriage : she would marry Cartwright and in marrying Cartwright she would marry the shop. In London she saw her life foreshortened by the dark walls of Cannon Street. In Evensford it opened out : bright, infinite, prosperous. In Evensford anything could happen. She saw Evensford, as represented by the shop, the parochial angularity of Mrs Cartwright and the empty rainy street, as a little town populated only by little people, and she knew that the littleness of it could not frustrate her.

'When do you plan to start with us, Miss Cassell ?'

'Tomorrow ?—when you like,' she said.

'I'm glad to hear it,' Mrs Cartwright said. 'We have been grossly understaffed since Miss Garvin married that man.'

'Tomorrow then ?'

'Friday is very busy. They are paid here on Fridays. We shall be glad of all the help we can. By the by, there are four other girls besides yourself. Miss Johnson, Miss Clark, Miss Dickins and Miss Hustwaite. We open at half-past eight and close at seven on ordinary nights. Eight on Fridays and nine on Saturdays. Are you chapel ?'

'I——'

'We are chapel ourselves,' Mrs Cartwright said.

'Yes.'

'I try to attend once every Sunday. Fred goes twice, sometimes three times. He is in the choir. We have a good many musical Sundays. It is rather a musical town.'

'Miss Cassell plays the piano,' Cartwright said.

'Oh, yes. Oh ! indeed ?' Mrs Cartwright said. 'That will be useful.'

'Very,' Cartwright said. 'Very. I——'

'Don't sprawl on the table, Fred ! You've got jam on the sleeve of your coat as it is. Put yourself in Miss Cassell's place for a moment. I wonder what she thinks of you.'

Cartwright sat silent, meek and overcome, rubbing the sleeve of his jacket with his hand and then licking his fingers.

'And don't lick your fingers ! Go upstairs and wash ! And before you go to choir-practice put on a clean collar. It looks disgraceful.'

Miss Cassell sat silent. She sat silent for most of the rest of that evening, she on one side of the fire in the sitting room, Mrs Cartwright on the other, Cartwright out at choir-practice. The rain fell heavily all evening and she could hear it running down the roof pipes in the long silences.

About nine o'clock she said good night and went to bed. Going upstairs she felt something run past her legs. It was the white cat. She caught it in her hands and held it against her blouse, in the crook of her arm, and took it into her bedroom. She undressed by the light of the street lamp that shone through the window, and while she undressed herself the cat lay curled on the bed. She got into bed and the cat lay with her, quiet against her shoulder. She lay awake for a long time, watching the rain, lemon and silver from the street-light, slowly pouring down the window panes beyond the curtains, listening to the sound of feet splashing past on the wet pavement below and to the sound of the rain, and thinking of Cartwright, of the man as she knew him and of the man she had seen that day. Thinking, she lay perfectly still, like the cat. Her eyes were made more grey and cool by the wet light falling on them from outside, the preoccupation of them not sad or regretful because she had come to the empty streets of a little town like Evensford, but simply preoccupied, detached and unemotional as the eyes of the cat lying at her side.

L

CARTWRIGHT HAD SOMETIMES made fussy, eager attempts to kiss her when they met in London. Now, as the spring came on and moved towards summer, he made still more eager attempts to kiss her, on the stairs or in the stock-room or at the back of the shop. And in a cool, unawakened way she would let him kiss her and she did not mind.

When Cartwright kissed her it did not mean very much to her. The daily life of the shop was very strict. Mrs Cartwright sat in the centre of the shop at the cash-desk, from which radiated the wires of the new cash-and-change system that Cartwright had recently installed. Like the criss-crossed wires of a toy overhead railway, the system covered completely the two floors of Cartwright's, the little cash receptacles flying smoothly and noisily over the counters, to and from the black figure of Mrs Cartwright, the person who really governed them. No one who came into or left the shop escaped the eyes of the woman watching through the windows of the cash-desk. The eyes turned themselves, cold and brown and rather sick, on every movement of the assistants too. The long pale yellow hands reached out and checked the figures of every account. So when Cartwright kissed her on the stairs in the house, or in the stock-room, away from the eyes of his mother, there was an air of secrecy which should have excited her. But for some reason or other she did not feel excited. She knew that she had no thought of falling in love with Cartwright. His kisses were rather wet and brief, and it seemed to her that he was like a boy who eats jam in a dark pantry when his mother is no longer there to see. On the other hand she did not resist Cartwright. Whenever he wanted to kiss her, whether it was in the shop or between the street-lights under the lime-trees as they walked back together from choir-practice late at night, her lips were always there, cool and smooth as paper and almost as lifeless. Her eyes were always open, looking passively past his face, far into air.

All that summer she did the work that was expected of her at Cartwright's, and she behaved as if she liked it. Outside the shop too she did the things that were expected of her, and she behaved also as if she liked them. She sang in the choir with Cartwright and played the piano at the mid-week practices. It was the day of outings in wagonettes on summer Saturday afternoons. She went on many of these outings with Cartwright, with the choir or the teachers of the Sunday school or the Order of Rechabites or the shop assistants of the town. They drove through miles of dusty gentle countryside, through small brown stone villages on the upper reaches of the river, where fishermen sat bent over rods in the becalmed afternoons. She always sat still and rather erect and rather aloof. When Cartwright asked her if she liked it she would say that she liked it. But always, whether on the outings or in the shop or in the house, her eyes looked away from Cartwright when she answered him. They seemed sometimes to have an immunity from all emotion. They seemed like the eyes of someone living an utterly separate life.

Cartwright, for whom there were two lives, the life of domination by his mother and the life of secret moments with Miss Cassell, did not notice this. He had begun to fall in love with Miss Cassell some time before she came to Evensford. He thought of her as rather select : too good for the parochial commonness of the small, one-street town. He was pleased by her, and excited by her, as he would be by a new model from London. She was not only very different from all that Evensford stood for. He knew that other people thought of her too like that. That pleased him. It showed him to be, after all, a man of good taste and sane enterprise, and he felt flattered. Not many young men went far out of Evensford for a girl, and his love for her had a kind of tender pride. He was rather surprised about it too. He was surprised that whenever he wanted her she was there, that whatever he wanted to do she too wanted to do. He was surprised by the passive docility of a person who, all that summer, had not made another friend.

They came home late one August evening from an outing when it was very hot and the wagonette was white with dust and she could feel the dust in her throat and hair. They went into the side-door of the house, and as they stood in the passage Cartwright kissed her. 'My lips are dusty,' she said. 'I feel dust all over. What time is it ?' He said it was past eleven o'clock and she said she would like a drink before she went to bed. The house was very silent and they talked in whispers. 'Go up now,' he said, 'and I'll bring you a drink. Some lemonade.'

She went upstairs and lay on the bed, not undressing, her arms outstretched. On very many nights the cat lay there, waiting for her, but tonight she lay on the bed alone, thinking. The street-light was out, and it was very dark in the room and when Cartwright came upstairs he had taken off his shoes and made no noise. He shut the door of the room as he came in and she felt him put the glass against her face. It was cool and she drank slowly. Then she gave him the glass and said 'You,' and Cartwright drank a little and then put the glass on the chest-of-drawers. A moment later she felt him lie on the bed beside her. She felt him put his hand on her throat and try to unclasp the velvet band she was wearing. At last it came away and he ran his hand down her long clear neck and then kissed her again. She felt his hands moving up and down her body and she let them move wherever Cartwright wanted, passive, unexcited by whatever he did. She let it go on for a long time without speaking. And then finally she turned her face on the pillow and spoke to him. 'You know if you do this you'll have to marry me ? Sooner or later. One day ?'

'Yes,' he said. 'I know. That's what I want. That's why I came.'

'I don't want you to go on if you don't want that. If you don't know.'

'I do want it. I do know. It's what I've always wanted. Always. Haven't you ? Haven't you ?'

Her eyes looked past him and remained fixed in the darkness broken only by the very faint light of the summer stars.

'Yes,' she said. 'It's what I've wanted.'

THEY WERE MARRIED in the October of that year and it was as if the marriage also meant nothing to her. As before, she continued to work in the shop. She was cool and efficient and if anything rather more aloof. As before, from the cash-desk with its neat system of wires, Mrs Cartwright, the mother, dominated everything.

And as before, the younger Mrs Cartwright seemed to let herself be dominated. She was quite obedient and docile. It seemed as if there were nothing she wanted. She went on doing whatever was expected of her, as if she liked doing it, the same as ever. When Cartwright wanted her to go out with him she went ; when he wanted her to play hymns for him on Sunday evenings she played them on the piano in the drawing-room ; whenever he wanted her she was ready and he could take her.

The weather that winter was very cold and the wind whipped

bitterly into the shop from the frozen street whenever the door was open. It cut into the pigeon-hole of the cash-desk where the elder Mrs Cartwright sat with her coat buttoned about her neck.

One morning when the assistants came in to work Mrs Cartwright was not at the cash-desk. Upstairs, in the elder Mrs Cartwright's bedroom, the two women were talking.

'Two days in bed and you will be yourself again.'

'I will not be told what to do and what not to do and I will not stay in bed.'

'If you get up it may eventually mean a week in bed.'

'I've never had a week in bed in my life !'

'You look very poorly and I think you're running a temperature. But, anyway, we'll see what the doctor says.'

'Doctor ? Doctor ?'

'Yes. I sent for him. Fred and I agreed that it would be better.'

'You've no right to do that ! You've no right !'

'Fred has a right,' the girl said. 'You don't want to die, do you ?'

'Die ? Die ? Who's going to die ? I am not going to die and I don't want a doctor.'

'All right,' she said. 'If you don't want a doctor no one can make you have one. I'll send Maisie to tell him not to come.'

The doctor did not come that day or the next and on the afternoon of the second day Mrs Cartwright got out of her bed and walked about the shop, staring at the assistants with sick brown eyes. After some time she began to walk up the shop stairs to the upstairs department. She walked very slowly, clinging to the banisters with one hand, and she was half-way up the stairs when she fell down.

For six weeks Mrs Cartwright lay in bed, and now she looked like an old shrunken woman. Each day she asked to get up. 'With rheumatic fever ?' the doctor said. 'Don't you value your heart ? It's the heart that has to be watched with this thing.' There was nothing much she could say in answer to that and the old look of domination in her eyes was very small.

All the time, downstairs, in the shop, though she was not to know of it until the day she shuffled down in her dressing-gown, groping from chair to counter like a person who could not see, there was a new source of domination. It was as if the younger

Mrs Cartwright had suddenly woken up. It was she now who sat in the cash-desk. It was she now who shut herself in the rear office on Thursday afternoons and, while Cartwright himself slept, went slowly and with methodical concentration over the books.

On these afternoons, when she had finished the books for the week, she would go back over the books for the year, and then for many years. There gradually formed in her mind a picture of the history of the shop. She saw how it had grown from being in 1880 a little millinery business carried on in the front parlour of the newly-married Cartwrights. She saw how it had grown from this one room to its first shop, with two rooms above, in a side street, and so from the side street to the main street in 1900. She saw how it had grown up with Evensford, selling what Evensford wanted. She saw in the change of handwriting in the ledgers the mark of the elder Cartwright's death and then the long smooth sequence of pages never damaged or broken until now, at last, she had changed them herself.

In this same way, relentlessly simple and efficient, she took over the rest of the shop. For years the windows had been dressed by Cartwright every Monday morning : drab, over-crowded, old-fashioned, safe. Now she began to dress them herself. She did things that began to startle Evensford. She began to change the window on Fridays ; it gave colour to the eyes of people who were paid on Fridays. She began to give Evensford styles and patterns that Evensford had only dreamed about and for a time did not want. And during these weeks of change it seemed to Cartwright that she was very wonderful.

Finally when the elder Mrs Cartwright came downstairs again the young Mrs Cartwright's change had become part of the routine and tradition of the shop. The old woman stood in the shop, one hand on the counter, the other holding the shawl about her neck, and looked at the changes there and tried to protest. She opened her mouth, but her teeth were not in, and the dark cavity of the mouth looked weak and old. The brown, once dominating eyes roved weakly to and fro and blinked as if they could not see. The long thin fingers, quivering and jerking spasmodically, looked blue and scaly and dead like the feet of a dead chicken.

'It's all right, mother. Ida is taking care of things,' Cartwright said. 'You're not strong yet. You've got to remember your heart. You've got to leave things more to Ida now.'

AFTER THAT it was only the heart of the elder Mrs Cartwright that expressed any domination in the changing shop. The weakened heart dominated all she felt, or did or wanted to do. 'With a heart like yours,' Cartwright said, 'you can't do quite as you used to do.' So she no longer did the books or sat in the cash-desk or helped to buy and sell the things for the shop. She came into the shop sometimes and sat behind the counter and with frail jerky hands cut off a length of ribbon and twined it crudely about her fingers. She sat for a time and talked to the people she knew.

The former Miss Cassell did not know anybody in Evensford whom she could talk to over the counter. She did not want to know anybody she could talk to. In four years she had come no closer to Evensford than on the first rainy afternoon when she had walked, lonely and disappointed, up the deserted street. She did not want to come any closer than that. After four or five years she did not feel that she loved Cartwright any more than on the day he had first kissed her, and she knew that she would not love him now. She could not in fact remember having loved anyone and certainly, she thought, there is no one in Evensford who will ever trouble me.

After three years the elder Mrs Cartwright had to be pushed about in a bath-chair and sometimes on fine afternoons, in the first slack hour after lunch, the young Mrs Cartwright pushed her through the main street of Evensford as far as the edge of the town. From that point, beyond the end of the railway, you could see the green meadows of the river valley and the red and blue town, and scattered along the far valley-side and after heavy rain the floods that lay like a lake, pearl-grey with the sea-gulls, between. For a few moments the two women would gaze across the valley and then, not speaking, turn back. Going back through the town the young Mrs Cartwright would stop the bath-chair from time to time so that people could speak to the elder Mrs Cartwright. As they spoke, kind, considerate, compassionate, gossipy, foolish, she stood behind the bath-chair and grasped the handle formally with her hands and kept herself aloof and silent. There was no one in Evensford to whom she wanted to be kind or considerate or compassionate. There was no one with whom she wanted to gossip, and most of all she was not a fool.

One afternoon in the late winter of the fourth year she had been at Evensford she pushed Mrs Cartwright to the edge of the town. The wind blowing over the dark edge of the valley was icy, driving with it sharp spits of rain. 'Are you cold?' the former Miss Cassell said.

'I am a little cold.'

'I don't think it will hurt you.'

'I would like to go back.'

'I don't think it will hurt you.'

She stood with her hands grasping the back of the bath-chair, gazing across the valley. She was not thinking of Mrs Cartwright, but of the shop. What she wanted had begun to take shape in her mind. Below, across the valley, the many sea-gulls rose and fell in the wind above the waters. She watched them vaguely. What she saw in reality was the shop enlarging and extending itself : another window, perhaps two windows, another floor, a whole new fitting department, a rest room, perhaps a café. Her eyes were cold in the wind and grey and distant with calculation. She did not feel the rain. What she felt was the rosy impact of a dream. No one, looking at the cold grey blank eyes, could have told how warm and excited she was. No one could have told what she was thinking : how gradually, by calculated stages, she would take the shop away from the Cartwrights and make it her own.

She must have stood there, gazing at the gulls on the water, for a long time. When she came to herself the elder Mrs Cartwright was crying. The sharp cold rain was beating harshly into her face and she was crying like a child : 'Take me back. I keep asking you. I'm so cold. I keep asking you. I keep asking you.'

Slowly, not speaking, the younger Mrs Cartwright turned the bath-chair and pushed it back to the town.

By the following Sunday they were offering prayers in the chapel for the recovery of the elder Mrs Cartwright. In the evening the younger Mrs Cartwright sat at the back of the chapel, in the gas-light, and leaned her head on the hard cool rim of the pew. She did not close her eyes ; she was not troubled. The words of appeal and prayer floated past her. 'Oh, Lord ! Oh,

Lord ! Look down on us and remember us. But remember we beseech Thee above all Thy servant who lies so ill at this time.' They were words which might have concerned someone she did not know and had never known.

In the morning she-stood at the window of her bedroom and watched two men spreading straw across the street below. It was raining and there was no wind and in the dark morning air the wide band of new wet straw shone brightly. The horse traffic drove over it and the hoofs and wheels had a rustling ghostly sound.

In the shop the assistants did not talk much. The working of the overhead cash-carrying system had ceased. It was strangely silent. The two elder assistants, Miss Johnson and Miss Dickins, who had been with the Cartwrights for fifteen years, came to work in shoes with rubber soles. They worked upstairs a great deal and that day you could not hear them walking overhead. After lunch Miss Johnson, who was short-sighted and wore spectacles, began to cry. The tears misted her spectacles and she could not see, and finally she cried for a long time alone in the stock-room.

All that day people came into the shop to ask, in whispers, how the elder Mrs Cartwright was. The shop-keepers of the street ran in for a moment and whispered. Towards evening the doctor came again, for the third time, and seeing him Miss Johnson burst into tears again and the shop was full of the painful sound of her crying.

The young Mrs Cartwright did not understand the tears or the solicitude ; and both, especially the tears of Miss Johnson, annoyed her. 'Everyone has to die,' she said to Miss Johnson, 'Do you want her to live and suffer ?'

She walked about the shop with calm unexalted face, speaking in her normal voice. Why should she change because someone else was dying ? Did it matter if she was the only person in Evensford who did not care whether a grey, wasted, suffering woman died or not ? She was outside the life of Evensford. The elder Mrs Cartwright had given it the clothes and hats and underwear and fashions it wanted. They were the things that the former Miss Cassell hated : the old, shabby, out-of-date, ridiculous things that were part of the soul of a little town. She despised them and now, like Mrs Cartwright, they were passing,

Another thing she did not understand was the feeling of Cartwright himself. He sat all day with his mother, watching her. He ate meals of biscuit and hot milk and did not come down into the shop. He walked about like a small boy who has lost the key of a clock-work toy and knows that the toy will not work any more. Seeing him, it occurred to her that Cartwright loved his mother. It even occurred to her now that Mrs Cartwright might have loved her son. The curious ways of affection defeated her. She remembered the tyranny of Mrs Cartwright at the dining table. 'Fred, you're not eating enough. Take a little more, take a little more ! Go on, go on. And pick up your napkin !' She remembered the impatient despair, the domination, the refusal to see Cartwright as a man. 'Sometimes I think you'll never grow up.'

Now she knew that Mrs Cartwright had never wanted her son to grow up ; that the tyranny and the domination were her way of preserving an image and a dream. That too was something which seemed to her weak and ridiculous. The basis of love was not tyranny ; certainly it was not illusion ; certainly not a dream.

That evening, as she sat alone in the drawing-room, Cartwright came downstairs. He shut the door of the room silently and stood by the fireplace. She knew by his silence that something had happened. She sat with the white cat on her lap but she did not get up.

'Mother has gone,' he said.

She did not speak. He stood pitifully looking down at her, spreading out his white trembling shop-keeper's hands.

'Aren't you going to say something ?'

She stroked the white cat with her hands, not speaking.

'Aren't you going to say anything ? Aren't you going to say you're sorry ?'

She still did not speak. She went on stroking the cat and she was not sorry. Now the tyranny and the domination and the old-fashioned ways and the stupidity were at an end, and she was simply glad that they were at an end.

THE FOLLOWING YEAR the Great War began. Already the shop had extended a little. Already the young Mrs Cartwright had had her first experience in buying property.

She enjoyed buying the shop next door. It was a narrow one-windowed shop kept by a single lady who sold confectionery and newspapers, and it was bought against the wishes of Cartwright. 'Why do we want to extend? We can't turn Miss Sturgess out, either. That would be wrong.'

'There are plenty of places for a person like Miss Sturgess. Evensford is full of them. That's what it's made of.'

She enjoyed all that summer. The feeling of destroying a tiny piece of Evensford and putting herself in its place: she felt that it was the first time she had been happy in Evensford. She liked the feeling of being strong enough, and free enough, and having money enough, to put into execution a tiny section of a dream.

All the time, as she tried to change the shop, Cartwright was trying to preserve it as he had known it. Every change obscured by a fraction the memory of his mother. His life was measured now by the life she had governed. 'When mother was alive,' he would say. 'Mother always used to say. It was mother's way of doing things.'

She did not tell him that she felt angry about this. She did not say that she thought it foolish, that she despised it or that it made her impatient. She only said, one day in the second year of the war: 'You seem so restless. Is it the war? Do you feel you ought to be doing something?'

'You think I ought to go?' he said.

'You have to do what you think.'

'I don't know what I think,' he said. 'Sometimes I think it right and sometimes I think it wrong.'

'You only have to do what you think is right.'

'I wonder what mother would have thought,' he said. 'I wonder.'

'It would have been different if she had been alive and she was the only one to be left,' she said. 'But I shall be all right. I'm young. You know you can leave me and I will be all right.'

'Are you sure?' he said. 'I would rather volunteer than be made to go.'

'I would like you to volunteer,' she said. 'I'd like that too. It's better.'

So at the end of the second year of the war Cartwright volunteered, and in the evenings, after the shop was closed, she was completely alone in the shop except for the maid in the kitchen and the white cat lying curled in the chair once occupied by the elder Mrs Cartwright and later by Cartwright himself. There was nothing for her to do now except read and sometimes play the piano, and think. Twice and sometimes three times a week she walked in the evenings to the public library. One or two people spoke to her on her way. The librarian said 'Good evening.' But no one stopped with her. She walked silently round the shelves in the library, choosing her books. The books were frowsy and tattered. Then she walked back to the shop and sat alone again, reading, sometimes with the cat on her lap. She was alone, but not lonely, and sometimes she ceased being absorbed by the book and looked up and stared into space, the grey eyes absorbed by calculation. She dreamed once again of how, after the war, the shop would grow, how completely she would revolutionise it, how it would become the foremost shop in Evensford. It did not once trouble her that she had no friends or children. The shop was the only friend she needed. She would see it grow up like a child.

It did not trouble her very much when, in the fourth year of the war, Cartwright was killed. She did not cry. Miss Johnson and Miss Dickins, the elderly assistants, again annoyed her by crying a great deal. But Miss Johnson and Miss Dickins were, she thought, old now. They belonged to the past phases of the shop. It was time too for them to go. 'Or you may stay on for less money,' she said. So the two elderly, now grey-haired women stayed on for the remaining year of the war for less money than the Cartwrights had paid them for ten years. They lived in lodgings together ; the war food was bad and they did not eat enough. They had feeble, quiet, courteous voices and they remembered the dresses and hats and materials that customers had bought over many years, and so customers liked to be served by them again and again. 'But a business is a business,' the young Mrs Cartwright said. 'There comes a time when we have to make changes.' The two elderly assistants cried again and Miss Dickins said, 'We have been here for twenty years. There is nowhere else for us. Nowhere. Nowhere now.'

When they had gone at last not only the customers but the travellers missed Miss Dickins and Miss Johnson. The travellers liked a joke with the two shy elderly ladies behind the counter.

It had become part of the tradition of the house. It was like the ceremonious procedure of giving an order. For many years the travellers had been invited into the Cartwrights' living room behind the shop, and they looked forward to coming there and staying there, talking and showing their samples over a piece of caraway cake and a cup of tea. Now they were terrified by the young Mrs Cartwright.

'Yes, I know we've been buying it at six-three. But you can come down.'

'I don't see how I can, Mrs Cartwright.'

'Oh! very well. Either you want the order or you don't want it. That's your affair. I'll say good afternoon.'

'Wait a minute, Mrs Cartwright, wait a minute.'

'I'm rather tired of waiting minutes.'

'Yes, but—we've always dealt with you fairly, Mrs Cartwright —we've—I'll tell you what—I'll make it six. That's a big drop. I oughtn't to do it on my own, Mrs Cartwright, but——'

'All right. A hundred dozen at six.'

'All right, Mrs Cartwright, yes.'

'As June 1st.'

'But that's three months, Mrs Cartwright !'

'I'm quite aware of it. Otherwise I shouldn't say so.'

She liked the feeling of victory over the travellers. They began by being so buoyant ; they ended by being so cast-down. She despised the old soft way of doing business : the cup of tea, the cake and the courtesies, the gossip, the shaken hand. She sat now behind the office desk, cold, rather stern, more dominant than the old Mrs Cartwright had ever been, and got from the experience of beating down a tired commercial traveller by a farthing a feeling of concealed exultation. She got something of the same feeling every afternoon as she walked to the bank with the day's takings. She walked down to the bank every afternoon at the same time, carrying the black cash-bag. It would be just before three in the afternoon and the street would be fairly crowded. She knew that people watched her. She wanted them to watch her. She liked and hated the curious looks of inquisitive unfriendliness on their faces. And she knew too that they hated her because they did not know her. She knew that a little town hates everyone whose business it does not know.

At the bank they gave her all the courtesy due to a growing

account. But she felt that the cashiers were snobs and that they too hated her. So she enjoyed raising her voice at them and making them jump. She liked querying a figure or demanding a pass-book late in the afternoon, when the bank was closing. She began to like more and more the feeling of power and exultation that money gave. When the books she got from the library were not what she wanted she liked to go into the office and check over and dream over the figures in the ledgers. She would be alone except for the white cat curled on the floor at her feet, and there would be no sound except the gas hissing in the burner over the desk. She liked to go back over the years and see how the business had grown. It had begun with a capital of ten pounds and in the first year the Cartwrights were happy because they made a profit of a pound a week from the sale of buttons on cards, ribbons, hat trimmings, shirt flannel and such things. The needs of Evensford were simple then. Now the turnover of the business was, in spite of war, practically five thousand a year, and it had not really begun to grow as she knew it could grow. The needs of Evensford might have been simple once ; she had seen to it that they were no longer so simple now.

As she sat there one evening, going over the accounts in the gaslight, she did not notice that the white cat was not in the room. The war was over now ; the papers were talking loudly about an era of reconstruction. She had been in Evensford ten years ; she was thirty-three ; much had happened. But it was nothing, she thought, to what was going to happen. An era of reconstruction was right : her own reconstruction, the reconstruction of the shop. The reconstruction of the world outside did not matter.

As she sat there she began to hear, above the hissing of the gas, another sound. She lifted her head and listened. She heard the sound of the cat crying gently somewhere beyond the window.

She got up and went out of the side door into the alley-way. The cat was trying to crawl on its belly by the wall. It was crying with pain. She picked it up in her arms and took it from the dark alley-way into the house. It was sick in her hands as she carried it. Her heart was beating very fast with the shock of the discovery : the first time she had ever felt it beating like that since she had been in Evensford.

She washed her hands of the sickness and then washed the face of the cat with warm water. It lay in her arms, not moving for some time. Suddenly it gave violent spasmodic jerks and began to cry feebly. It jerked violently again and fell out of her lap, beating its head on the floor. She picked it up and hugged it desperately to her. She felt slightly hysterical and did not know what to do. Every time the poison lacerated the cat with pain she felt a sudden laceration inside herself. For the first time she discovered that the sufferings of another creature could hurt her terribly. As the bitter, difficult and painful tears came into her eyes she felt more and more helpless. The cat struggled more violently. 'Oh, please ! Oh, please !' she said. 'Oh, please ! Please God don't let it suffer.'

She carried the cat round and round the room in her arms like a sick child, crying bitterly, feeling more and more helpless, knowing less and less what to do. Then she carried it upstairs and lay down on the bed with it, as she had done on her first night in Evensford and had done so many times since. Every time the cat struggled in her arms she felt the anguish of it tearing her own body into thin raw strips of pain.

'Oh, please, please don't let it ! Please God don't let it suffer. Please let it die. Please. Please God don't let it live and suffer.'

She lay there all night with the cat in her arms. After it died she did not get up and she did not sleep, but simply lay staring in the darkness. She forgot the unlocked safe and the doors she always so carefully locked downstairs. She forgot the ledgers and the accounts and the money. They all seemed suddenly of little importance now.

SHE DID NOT GET OVER the pain of the cat's death for quite a long time. It became part of a new kind of hatred for Evensford : as if Evensford itself had deliberately poisoned the only thing for which she cared.

She felt very lonely too. She began to get more easily angry with people. Miss Dickins and Miss Johnson had gone. Now, one by one, she found some excuse to get rid of the other assistants. She walked round the shop like a woman with an invisible dagger in her hands. She hated the giggling, whispering, dowdy girls behind the counters. She wanted to stick the dagger into someone. She hated more and more the dead little town.

The shop next door was owned by a couple named Jordan,

who sold confectionery and toys.   Old Mrs Jordan suffered from
asthma and sometimes you could hear the agony of her coughing
in the front bedroom above the shop.   Mr Jordan treated her
with great care and took her away to Bournemouth for a fortnight
every summer.   Both Mr and Mrs Jordan were thin and small,
and when they walked out together they looked as if they were
propping each other up.   The impression was that when one went
away the other would fall down.

That summer, the second after the war, Mr Jordan did not
take Mrs Jordan to the sea.   She died on a hot stifling day in
August.   She fought in vain and in agony for her breath in the
sweltering little bedroom that lay low under the rafters of the
old-fashioned shop.   After her death old Mr Jordan walked
about as if he were leaning on the air and would fall over.   'She
couldn't get her breath,' he kept saying.   'If only she could have
got her breath.   If only she could have got her breath.'

The Jordans were typical of Evensford.   They did as everyone
else did.   Every Sunday morning Mr Jordan took a small batter
pudding, in a flat baking tin, to be cooked in the bakehouse
round the corner.   In the centre of the yellow batter was a small
piece of red beef, and on the beef was a ticket, pinned by a long,
blue-headed pin, to say whose pudding it was.   While the meat
and the pudding were cooking Mr and Mrs Jordan went to
church.   Mr Jordan always took the pudding at twenty-five
minutes to eleven.   He was always very punctual, so that people
going to church knew they were not late if they saw Mr Jordan
with the pudding.

After Mrs Jordan's death he did not take the pudding.   It
was as if he no longer had any interest in keeping alive.   The
day of Mrs Jordan's death he pinned a written notice on the shop
door.   'Temp. closed owing to decease of partner.'   It remained
a fortnight.

Towards the end of the fortnight Mrs Cartwright called on
Mr Jordan.   She called at the back door of the house.   She
was met by a Mr Jordan she had never seen before.   He had not
shaved and his hair was uncombed and his eyes were choked with
dried yellow lumps of matter.   His tongue hung out a little and
the nails of his hands were long and black.

He peered at her blindly through the crack of the door.

'Uh?' he said.

'I came to see how you were,' she said. 'I came to see you about something.'

'Uh?'

'I came to talk to you about something.'

'Me? You want me? Uh?'

'Could I come in?'

Mr Jordan opened the door very slowly and let her in. In the living room the cloth was dirty on the table. Dirty cups and plates, bread and jam, old newspapers were scattered about it. Mr Jordan made an attempt to pile the dirty cups and plates together, and then gave it up. He looked as if he were going to fall down.

'Uh? Want see me, uh?' he said.

'Mr Jordan,' she said, 'you haven't opened the shop. Aren't you going to open it? Perhaps you're not going to keep it on?'

'Uh?' he said.

'The shop,' she said. She tried to explain carefully. She was irritated by the stupidity of an old man who seemed unable to think. The house made her sick. She hated the sour stale smell of the greasy table. She had no patience with the old yellow eyes and the dirty trembling hands.

'If you're not going to keep it on,' she said, 'I would buy it.'

'Uh?'

'I would buy it,' she said. She tried to explain carefully again. She was irritated because she did not know whether his head was nodding or trembling. 'You need a rest,' she said. 'I'd make you a good offer if you'd sell.'

'Sell?'

'I'll offer you five hundred for the freehold, and another hundred for the stock.'

'Uh?'

He kept staring emptily at her with yellow watery eyes. She grew more and more irritated. She hated the dirty greasy little room and the smell of cheap sweets, warm and stale, that came from beyond the bead curtain in the doorway leading to the shop: just another piece of Evensford, dead, stupid, out of date. It was dead and she would tear it down.

'It's a good offer,' she said.

'She couldn't get her breath,' he said.

M

She wanted to strike the old stupefied face into understanding. 'It's a good offer,' she said. 'Don't you understand ?'

She stayed there all afternoon. She knew that he did not understand. He did not seem to care about time or understanding or even the shop. Only once he asked, as if it were established fact that she would buy :

'You goin' keep it on like it is ? Sweets and that ? Good trade, you know. Sometimes we——'

'Yes,' she said. 'Yes. I'll keep it on.'

'Like it is, uh ?'

'Yes,' she said. 'Like it is.'

'Long as I know that,' he said.

She knew that he had no understanding of what it was all about. She made her promises to him with grey steady eyes full of calculation. She smoothed her gloves with her fingers and then bent the fingers and admired the smoothed tight hands.

In three days she had bought the shop. In three or four weeks the builders were pulling it down. She liked to stand outside and watch the raw hole growing wider in the street. She liked the idea of the clean autumn wind driving through the gap. Above all she liked the clean feeling in herself. She felt renewed and happier. Even the cat did not seem to matter. She thought more and more of herself again.

IN A YEAR OR TWO the shop as the Cartwrights had known it was no longer there. The front was lengthened ; wide windows opened to a circular arcade, where people could shelter from the rain. Upstairs there was a café. Every two months the young Mrs Cartwright, already looking not quite so young, presented Evensford with a mannequin parade, and served tea and coffee and cakes without charge. She illuminated the windows at night, after the shop was shut. She kept the light burning until most of Evensford had gone to bed. Inside, the old system of dusty boxes on shelves had gone ; and the pine staircase ; and the clanking clumsy overhead railway for the cash. Gradually she had torn out the dark, dusty, ugly insides of the place. What now remained was select, cool, rather aloof : the expression of herself. The paint was bright and hard. You walked on soft carpets that were without friendliness.

During this time and for the next ten years she worked very

hard. She liked work. She liked acquiring something, changing it, effacing the recollection of what it had been. It became almost a mania with her to buy property everywhere in Evensford. Whenever there was a property sale she was there ; she sat at the back of the auction room, too conspicuous for Evensford, too well dressed, very alone, very aloof, not moving except for a flicker of her pencil as she raised the bidding. She bought mostly shops ; after that rows of working-class houses in the poorer parts of the town. She bought and then waited. She waited and then, on some trivial excuse, put up the rent. She liked that too. She liked the feeling of power : the deliberate, cool, unpleasant power of imposing herself on a town that did not want her.

She had been in Evensford for about thirty years when she bought a row of houses in Warren Street, a section of the town between the railway and the river. They were the sort of houses that made up more than half the streets of Evensford : flat, grim red little boxes fronting straight on to the street. The long flat frontage was split open by recurrent entries. The backyards, filled with dirty hen-runs and water-butts and clothes lines, were out of the sun.

She began to go every Friday to Warren Street, as she went to all the other houses she owned in Evensford, to collect the rent. In most houses the rent-money lay ready for her on the rent-book on the kitchen table. She knocked on the back door, went in, and took up the rent. She counted the money, signed the book and came out again. Sometimes people did not speak to her. She hated this feeling of hostility as she hated the over-crowded back-kitchens, with the washing drying under the ceiling and the men washing at the sinks and the mangle in the corner and the dirty roller towel on the door. She hated the stale smell of boiled onions and boot polish and drying napkins. She hated every part of the mean, fusty, overcrowded life.

In Warren Street the people were new to her. She did not know them. Yet she might have known them for ever. They were a replica of all the people in all the streets she had ever known in the town.

It was not until the third rent day that she found any difference in Warren Street. She went into the kitchen of Number 8 and at the table a man of about thirty was reading a book.

'Yes ?' he said.

'I've called for the rent,' she said.

'I don't know anything about it,' he said, 'I only lodge here.'

'Wasn't it left ? It's always left.'

'If it had been left,' he said, 'it would have been here.'

The man had black, direct, rather mocking eyes. He held his head in his hands as he read. His black hair fell on his hands. The book was on the table. He moved his head stiffly upwards as he spoke.

'You read a lot ?' she said.

'Quite a lot.'

As if to say, 'What has it to do with you ?'

'I'm afraid you'll find no bookshop in Evensford.'

'I found the library.'

'That place ?'

'That place,' he said.

'The books have all been there for years. Filthy. Out of date. I thought nobody ever went there now. It should have been pulled down long ago.'

'Like some of the houses,' he said.

'What did you say ?'

'You don't like Evensford, do you ?' he said.

'How do you know ?'

He looked at her, black eyes mocking but calm, sharp elbows jabbed against the table, chin forward.

'I can tell what people like and what they don't like.'

'You can ?' she said. 'Well, do you like Evensford ?'

'It's as good as any other working town.'

'Which means ?'

'Which means the working people live where they work and lump the place if they don't like it.'

'But you ? You can read anywhere ?'

'I can read anywhere.'

'You read quickly,' she said, 'don't you ?'

'I read pretty quickly.'

'You'll soon exhaust the poor little library at Evensford if you go too often.'

'Think so ?' he said. 'I hear there's five thousand books. Three times a week and I'll still be a long time.'

'You will.'

'I will,' he said.

He looked at her steadily for a moment as if to say 'Have you
finished with me?' and then, after a moment or two, she left.
She left without asking any more about the rent and he did not
get up from the table. Going down the backyards of the houses
she found herself trembling. No one had ever talked to her like
that.

TO BE INTERESTED in someone, to talk to someone, to
feel her interest in life filtering out beyond the shop : this was
new. It produced in her a feeling of rather troubled excitement.

She went to the library on the following evening and on the
evening after that, but the man from Warren Street was not there.
The library was in the old Church Rooms, where huge red cards
marked 'Silence' were placed on pale grim walls above the dark
shelves of books, and the quarter strokes of the church clock, very
near outside, beat down into the silence regularly. It was summer
and the evenings were light outside, but inside, between the dark
shelves, a gas lamp burned above the books. At the entrance the
librarian sat behind a pigeon-hole. The door into the shelves was
opened by a foot spring, and until you worked it you could not
get in or out. When you worked it the door slammed shut behind
you with a loud explosion in the silence, and it was as if you were
in a trap.

Mrs Cartwright came away from the library, and went again,
as if she were trapped : as if suddenly, completely without
warning and for the first time, she were trapped by something
outside herself and not of her own responsibility. At the shop
she went to bed with the books she had borrowed. She did not
even look at them. She lay and watched the light of the street
lamp on the ceiling and thought of the annoyance, the calm and
the sharp white elbows of the man in Warren Street. 'I can tell
what people like and what they don't like,' she remembered.

Did he also know what people were thinking and feeling ?
What she was thinking and feeling ? It occurred to her suddenly
that he might have stayed away from the library because he really
did know what she thought and felt and might do. 'I won't
go again,' she thought.

The following evening she stayed in the room behind the shop
until after nine o'clock. The library closed at ten. She felt very
restless. She tried for a time to play the piano. Finally she went

out of the back door and hurried down to the library as the church clock was striking half-past nine.

She did not know what to say to the man from Warren Street, who stood in the library under the gaslight, turning over the books. She felt more than ever as if she were trapped. Her eyes looked filmy and uncertain and had lost their look of calculation.

'Well?' he said. 'I thought nobody ever came here.'

'I come.'

'Often?'

'When I want something new.'

He put the book back on the shelf.

'What sort of things do you read?' she said.

'Detective stuff.'

'Only that?'

'Mostly that. Keeps me excited.'

'Life isn't very exciting for a stranger here, is it?'

'I told you it's like any working-class town,' he said. 'Pubs, pictures, chapels, shops. You ought to know. You've lived here. You're part of it.'

'Part of it? Me? You can live here for years and be a stranger.'

He picked up another book, glanced at her and turned over the pages.

'Why don't you go somewhere else if you don't like it?' he said.

'Somewhere else?'

'You've got money. You've got nothing to keep you. People let themselves get too complicated. All you've got to do is get up some morning and say "I've finished with this. I'll start afresh. Somewhere else." '

'Where?'

'Anywhere you like better.'

'Alone?'

He did not answer.

'Are you happy?' she said. 'I mean here? In a town like this?'

'I'm all right. I'm happy,' he said. 'I don't want much. I've got my job. I'm all right.'

She felt she had nothing to say. It was almost ten o'clock. They talked in very low voices. It was twilight beyond the windows and the librarian was packing up her papers.

'Haven't you got a book?' he said.

'Not yet. If you wait I'll get one.'

'It's closing time,' he said. 'Hadn't you better get one quickly?'

She took a book from the shelves, hurriedly, at random, not knowing what it was. 'We can go now,' she said.

'We?' He glanced at her, sideways, mocking a little.

'You could go my way. It's partly on your way.'

'Partly?' He had a way of smiling and then closing his eyes. The dark lids, pulled too smoothly down, seemed instantaneously to curl upward the too smooth full lips. When he opened his eyes again the smile remained for a moment or two fixed, softly ironical. It seemed to magnetize her.

They walked down the street in the darkening air: the hideous little street, with the flat brick houses, the bootshop next to the library, the slaughter-house opposite, the tea-shop with the fly-blown cakes in the window, the youths sprawling against the pillar-box on the corner. She did not notice any of it now. Before, coming alone from the library, she had always been conscious of the young men at the corner, looking her up and down. She had caught the faint odour of the slaughter-house, the smell of the stale cooking-fat from the little café. She had held her breath as she passed the people of Evensford coming up the High Street, late from the cinemas, fish-and-chips in their hands. She had felt her breath sour into a lump of sickness in her throat. She walked down the street now as if none of it existed.

In her own shop, in the new bright windows, the light was burning. The dresses on the models were like splashes of flower-light in the dark street. She stopped by the window. She gazed for a moment at the sharp clean light cast across the dusty summer pavement, the dirty gutter, the oil-stained roadway that shone like polished iron. She felt for a moment proud of it: her light, the light of an achievement. It looked smart and positive and fashionable. It had taken her many years to achieve that white clean glare across the pavement. She wished that he would notice it too.

He stood looking down the street, hatless, his black eyes rather sleepy and indifferent, as if he did not know she was there.

'Wouldn't you come in?' she said.

'It's late for you.'

'Oh, no ! Oh, no ! It really isn't.'

'Well——'

She found her latch-key and unlocked the door in the alley-way. She switched on the light in the passage inside and the old heavy smell of drapery was thick in the closed house. She switched on the light in the drawing-room and called him to come in. She was struck suddenly by the awful emptiness of the place. How long had it been since she had asked anyone into that room ? How did she come to live here alone ? She felt the loneliness of years, broken suddenly, stream down through her body in a cold shiver of excitement. Her hands were damp as she wiped them across her face.

'I don't know if you'd like something to eat ?' she said.

'Oh, no !'

'A drink or something ? An orange ? Have something please.'

'Oh, well, an orange,' he said.

'They're nice,' she said. 'I got them to-day. They're very nice. Take a good one.'

He sat on the sofa and took an orange from the dish on the table at his side. He rolled it in his hands, using the palms of his hands. His fingers were long and white and straight. They stood away from the orange, almost insolent. There was some-thing about their sleekness which kept her fascinated. It was very foolish, but it was as if he were going to do a conjuring trick and suddenly the orange would disappear and he would look up at her, with the lids of his eyes smoothly drawn down and the smooth ironical smile on his face, and say, 'You see ?—simple. Very simple. Quite simple. You see ?' All the time she sat fascinated and yet, in a way, hating it. All the time she felt the loneliness of years, dispelled, running through her body in excitement.

'What do you do in Evensford ?' she said. 'What does a person like you come to be doing here ?'

'I'm a teacher.' The smile spread slowly over his face. 'Train the child in the way it should go.'

He began to peel the orange. She saw the fine spray of juice squirt up from the pressure of his thumb on the skin.

'You'll ruin your suit,' she said.

'Suit ?' he said. 'What with ?—oh, that's nothing.'

'Nonsense,' she said. 'I'll get you a serviette. It's all over you.'

She went out of the room and brought back the serviette. She unrolled it and spread it on his knees. It seemed suddenly to her like an act of familiarity. It pleased her to do it, to give part of herself in service. He smiled a little, mocking, and let the golden sections of peel fall on the white cloth. Then he broke the orange in his fingers, and then broke the parts again. Then he began to eat it, taking the pips out of his mouth and holding them in his hands. He held them and looked at her, sideways, eyes half closed.

'There's a look on your face like the look of a small boy,' she said.

'Doing what?'

'Waiting.'

They looked at each other for a second or two, not speaking.

'Waiting for what?' he said at last.

'For the chance of doing something to somebody who isn't looking.'

He smiled ironically again.

'The pips?'

'The pips,' Mrs Cartwright said.

'Really?'

'Yes, really,' she said. 'As if you didn't know.'

She saw him rubbing the oily-wet orange pips in the tips of his slender fingers, and the gleam of juice on his hands. There was a look in his eyes of tender mockery as he looked straight at her.

'Dare me to,' he said.

'Just like a small boy?'

'Dare me to.'

'You daren't do it as a man. You want me to dare you to do it as a small boy. And then you dare do it, daren't you?'

'Just dare me,' he said.

'How old are you, playing with orange pips?'

'Twenty-five.'

'Just a small boy.'

'Dare me,' he said very softly. He rolled the orange pips slowly in the tips of his fingers. 'Dare me.'

They sat looking at each other for perhaps another thirty seconds, half smiling, waiting for each other.

'What will you do if I dare you?' she said.

'Dare me.'

'All right,' she said, as if she had suddenly become young and careless and stupid and utterly irresponsible for the first time in her life. 'Since you want me to.' She began to laugh now as she spoke. 'I dare you to.'

He squirted the first pip at her, from between his finger-tips, almost before she had finished speaking. She shrieked a little as it flew past her face. He shot another, and she picked up a cushion and held it in front of her face, and then she heard other pips bouncing on the cushion. 'I can see a lot of you besides your face,' he said.

'Oh, no, please, not my dress !'

She felt the pips begin to strike her body. They struck her softly on the breast and the bare arms, and they fell in her lap. She tried to pick them up so that the juice should not stain her dress, but the cushion fell as she did so and he began to shoot the pips again at her face. She was laughing and panting and she felt quite foolish and for some reason partly annoyed and partly happy. One of the pips struck her on the face and she begged him to stop. 'You dared me to,' he said. 'You know you dared me.'

'Yes, I know, but stop now.'

'You don't want me to stop,' he said. 'You like it. You're laughing.'

'Yes, I know, but stop.'

'You're laughing so much there are tears in your eyes.'

She lay back in her chair, looking at him through the soft film of tears brought on by laughter, her mouth open and her breath panting quietly through it, her hands loosely grasping the cushion to her body.

'Oh, dear ! Oh, heaven !' she said. 'I haven't laughed so much for years.'

He looked at her casually, smiling silently, eyes half closed.

'Oh ! it was really awfully silly,' she said.

She smoothed her dress awkwardly with her hands. He did not move. She patted her hands against her hair.

'Awfully silly,' she said. 'Awfully silly.'

'You dared me,' he said.

'Yes, I know. But you looked so like a small boy.'

She looked up at him, tenderly, but the expression on his face did not change. She suddenly felt embarrassed before the casual, ironical, almost pitying glance. The last of the orange had gone, and still looking at her he took his handkerchief and wiped his lips, then his fingers and then his lips again. Her embarrassment did not bring them any closer together. The expression on his face remained exactly the same : as if he were faintly amused by the sight of a woman of fifty panting with shyness, excitement and laughter.

'Well, I must go,' he said.

'Must you ?'

'I think so. I really think so.'

'Oh !'

He got up from the sofa, stretching his arms. She felt awkward and shy. She held her hands together and then dropped them by her sides.

'You'll come in again ?'

'Well——'

'Do you play the piano ?'

'I don't.'

'You could come to tea.'

'Some day,' he said.

She did not know what else to say. She walked with him to the door. She opened it and felt the night air cool on her face. The street outside was very quiet. She longed suddenly to walk down the dark streets, without her hat, to the other end of the town, and walk back alone and think of what had happened. She waited for a moment or two in silence, wanting him to speak. She wanted him to say how nice it had been, to be polite, to say thank you. He stood with his hands in his pockets, the book pressed under his arm. She could not see his face very clearly, but she felt she knew just how calm and careless it was. She hated it and was hurt by it at the same time.

'Good night,' she said. 'I hope you'll come in again. I do hope so.'

' 'Night,' he said.

He walked down the alley-way and into the street before she had time to speak again.

She shut the door and latched it and slowly walked upstairs. She sat down on the bed. Her hands were trembling. The light of the shop had been automatically switched out and the room was dark. She felt her loneliness, dispelled momentarily by the foolish behaviour downstairs, come back again. She lifted her trembling hands to her face, to comfort herself, and smelled the stale sweet odour of oranges on them still.

'WHY DO I LIVE in Warren Street?' he said. 'I thought you'd want to know that.'

He lay stretched on the sofa, his feet up. He had come to tea at last, on a Sunday. It was past the end of the summer.

'Why do you?' she said. 'You—living in that street.'

'You own it,' he said.

'But that's different.'

'Different? How is it different? You own it and I live in it—for the same reason.' He looked at her steadily, nonchalantly. 'Suppose I want money too? The cheaper I live the more I save.'

'Money? What good will money do you?'

'You ought to know,' he said.

'Yes, but you're young,' she said. 'You've got life. You don't need money.'

He looked at her, not smiling now.

'We lived in Birmingham,' he said. 'My father was a brass-foundry hand. There were eight of us. Brought up on thirty bob a week. Don't talk to me about not wanting money. I know what it is to want it. To want it terribly and not to get it. I know.'

'It isn't everything.'

'No,' he said, 'but it'll do as a substitute until I find something better.'

'That's awful talk,' she said.

'Awful?'

'To hear you say that—it's awful. You're young. Don't you see? Don't you ever think of anything else—friends, home, career, that sort of thing?'

'They'll come,' he said.

He reached out and took a cake from the table standing between the settee and her chair. He bit into it and took a mouthful of tea, washing it down. He wiped one hand across his mouth. She hated suddenly the nonchalant ill-manners, the cocksureness, the bright black eyes and their flash of superciliousness.

'I know what I want,' he said.

She sat staring at him. She despised what he said and yet she was fascinated by the voice which said it. As she sat watching him she found herself gradually becoming oblivious of the words he used.

All the time she was troubled by his neck-tie. The knot was loose and did not reach the collar of his shirt. She felt an extra-ordinary desire to knot it tightly. It needed a little invisible pin underneath it in order to keep it tight. It needed to be tied in just such a way that it would never loosen. She sat for a long time staring at it, knotting and re-knotting it in her imagination, her hand fretful and her ears oblivious to what he was saying, until she could bear it no longer.

She suddenly got up and went over to him and knelt by the sofa. She tried to make fun of what she was doing but her hands were trembling.

'Come here, do,' she said. 'Your tie is an awful sight.'

'Oh, my tie's all right,' he said. 'It's all right.'

'It isn't all right. It's awful. Just look at it. It's awful.'

He fingered it irritably.

'Don't touch it !' she said.

'Then why must *you* touch it ?'

'Because it looks awful. It's loose and you look a disgrace. Hold up your head.'

'God !' he said.

She began to tie the neck-tie softly and slowly, with finicky tenderness. He held his head away from her, irritated. She tied the neck-tie once and then undid it and began to tie it again.

'For heaven's sake,' he said.

'No,' she said, 'hold still. Please hold still. Just for a moment. Please.'

Her hands were close under his throat ; the fabric of the tie was smooth and soft.

'Must you do this ?' he said.

She went on knotting the tie, kneeling down before him. To do something for him, however small and however foolish, seemed suddenly an important thing. She leaned back and looked at the tie with warmth and pleasure in her eyes.

'Satisfied?' he said.

'Oh, please,' she said. 'Just one more second. Then it'll be perfect——' She stretched out her hands.

'Oh, Jesus!' he said.

'Please,' she said. 'Please. Just one moment. It's almost right. Be a good boy.'

'Boy!' he said. 'Boy! Is that all you think of me? Perhaps you'd like to brush my hair and clean my nails too?'

'I'd do even that,' she said.

'You women!' he said. 'You women.'

'All of us?' she said. 'Or only me?'

She leaned back on her knees, smiling, her eyes alight, teasing him.

'Oh! I don't know,' he said. 'I——'

'Now you're offended,' she said.

He got up suddenly from the sofa, leaving her there on her knees. He walked about the room, pulling his tie.

'Please don't be offended,' she said.

'Who's offended? Who's offended?'

'Don't be angry.'

'Who said I was angry?'

'Don't be angry any more.'

'I'm not angry!' he shouted. 'I just don't want to be fussed by you. I don't want to be touched by you. I've got something better to do than be fooled about by someone old enough to be my mother!'

She did not speak and she did not raise herself up from her knees. She sat staring at him as if she did not believe what he had said. Her mind felt wooden with pain and she was only half aware of him going out of the room, furiously banging the door of the hall, and of the abrupt and painful silence of the house.

That night she wrote a letter to him and went out, very late, to post it at the letter-box on the corner. It was raining and cold and the summer now seemed finally over. 'Please forgive me,' she said. 'Perhaps what I did seemed very foolish to you. It was not meant like that. Send me a word to say you don't think too badly of me. Just a word. It isn't much. It's a little thing.'

Autumn came on with cold gales of rain that brought down

and flattened wetly on the pavement the brown leaves of the street trees. She waited for an answer to the letter, but there was no answer.

SHE CONTINUED to go down to the library, borrowing books she never read, two and three and sometimes four evenings a week, all that autumn and on into the winter. The young man from Warren Street was never at the library ; she did not meet him in the street or when she collected the rent. She went to the library with the almost automatic hope that one evening she would grasp the handle of the glass swing doors on one side and he the other, and that each of them would try to pull the doors open and there would be a moment of deadlock before they smiled at each other through the glass. After that he would come to tea again. She would fuss round him and pour his tea and give him a serviette to wipe his fingers. It would be all right and she would be happy. She would be happy because for the first time for thirty years she was giving something to someone and not taking it away. Her eyes, as she stared at the books in the dim light of the library, had lost their look of calculation. When she thought of him she was struck by the incalculable force of little things : the pips of an orange, a neck-tie, a serviette. She thought of Cartwright, the elder Mrs Cartwright, the faded assistants of the shop, all dead now, from whom she had never had a moment of life that she herself had not calculated. None of them had left a fragrance of orange on her hands. None of them had ever filled more than a fraction of her life. She had been able to calculate their lives in relation to her own. She had almost been able to calculate the way they would die. When she lay awake at night and listened to the sounds of the trees and the feet in the street below, she was listening, in reality, to her own thoughts—always how she would acquire something, change it, progress a little further, calculate a little more. Now when she heard the last of the autumn leaves flapping wetly on the branches it was as if they fell damply and with monotony into the emptiness of her own mind. She lay awake all the nights of that autumn and listened to the leaves with an empty agony, and sometimes because she could not sleep she got up and stood by the window and pressed her head against the cold glass and listened to the rain streaming wildly down the cold face of the window as if it were her own infinite tears falling for the things she could not describe.

What she wanted now was very simple. To be given something, and not to take it, to be given not even affection but only the means of expressing it. She wanted something at last that she could not buy : the privacy, the privilege, the affection of another life. Was it, she thought, very much to ask ?

On the evenings when she did not go to the library she sat in the room behind the shop. She would sit staring at the fire and, staring, forget to make it up. She would get up and wander nervously about the room, stopping to touch the notes of the piano. Her shoulders felt cold. She did not want to eat. She remembered the time when she had not wanted to come close to Evensford and when she knew that no one in Evensford would ever trouble her.

Finally, because she could bear it no longer, she wrote another letter. 'I would like to try and explain a little what I feel. I hoped I would see you again. I know you were angry that day but there is no need to be angry. It isn't easy to explain what I feel. You must know that people grow fond of other people for the most unlikely reasons, and in a way that is the trouble. If I knew why I was fond of you it would be very simple. But I don't know. I just know that when I first saw you I felt differently from the way I'd ever felt about anyone before. I just don't know any other reason. I just want to sit with you and do things for you and talk to you and know that you like me. It isn't easy to explain. Perhaps it seems rather silly at my age to be saying this. Perhaps I ought not to say it. I don't know. It doesn't matter. I am writing this because it is so much easier to write it than to say it, and it does seem sometimes as if I shall never see you again. You are very young, but can you see what I mean ? I know that one often can't be bothered to understand when one is young. But if you can understand will you come to see me—please, some time ? Please will you ? You needn't stay long, and you needn't ever come again. But if you come I shall know that you understand.'

She wrote the letter at the close of the year. She had spent Christmas alone and the weather was very cold. Early snow turned to black slush in the streets and then froze again into crusts of black glass. The wind blew bitterly up the valley from the sea, and there were not many people at the library in the evenings. Mrs Cartwright felt the cold and wrapped a big brown woollen scarf over her head and tied it under her chin. It was colder than the days when the elder Mrs Cartwright had died. She wore an old fur coat because it was lined and warm. In the darkness it did not matter much.

She waited a fortnight but there was no answer. She went to the library every evening without seeing the man from Warren Street. She walked up and down between the shelves in a state of great distress. She took out books from the shelves and put them back again. The big red notices on the walls seemed to stare painfully down at her. The door of the library clicked open and closed with an awful hollow sound like a trap.

She went home alone every evening, wrapped against the cold in the big brown scarf and the old fur coat and went straight to bed. She knew now that there would be no answer. She began to feel now as she had done when the cat had died. All the isolation of the years she had spent in Evensford narrowed into a single prolonged experience of loneliness. Formerly she had not wanted the cat to suffer. Now she did not want to suffer herself.

When after three weeks there was no answer and it struck her finally that he might have gone away altogether, she got up out of bed one night and walked about the room in her bare feet, vaguely raising her hands to her face and letting them fall again. She felt all the emotions she had felt when the cat had died : the painful, difficult, blinding tears and the helplessness. She lay down on the bed and clutched the wooden bars of the bedstead with her hands and felt everything simplify into a moment of pure agony : the agony of knowing at last what was wrong and of knowing that nothing would put it right. To want someone and not be wanted : that was wrong. That was the explanation. 'Oh, God !' she said, 'Oh, God !' She muttered the words help-lessly and vehemently, as she had done when the cat had died : the same words, out of the same despair. 'Oh, God, don't let me live and suffer !'

She went on the following day to collect the rent at Warren Street. Snow lay on the asphalt backyards in crusty frozen heaps, and ice on the water-barrels by the back doors. She tried to be calm as she walked from house to house. The wind was cold and

N

beat her hair into her face untidily. The little backyards were treacherous and grim and bare and the cabbages were frozen in the gardens. She walked on the frozen snow with small agitated steps, exactly as if she were frightened and trembling.

What she wanted had become more simple than ever. She wanted him simply to be there, in the house, reading at the table in the living-room with his sharp white elbows on the table and his cool eyes lifted to recognize her. She wanted him simply to exist. It was a very simple unextravagant thing to want and it seemed strange that she had lived in Evensford for more than thirty years before it should happen.

When she saw the woman of the house and the table in the living-room empty except for the rent-book and the money lying on it she made a great effort to be calmer than ever.

'Has Mr— has your lodger gone?' she said. Her voice sounded stupid and false. She tried again. 'I mean—I——'

'Mr West?'

'Mr West,' she said.

'He's off to Birmingham again.'

'Again?'

'Been going there twice and three times a week this fortnight.'

'Working?'

'Working or playing, I don't know what you'd call it. Amounts to the same thing. Bringing his girl down and going to be married.'

'Here?'

'In the John Street Baptist next Thursday. They're coming back on the three train to-morrow.'

'That's very nice,' she said.

She walked out of the house and down the backyards, over the frozen snow.

THE AFTERNOON TRAIN came in to Evensford at 3.13; for thirty years it had come in at about the same time. Walking down to the station on the following day, wearing the brown scarf folded high under her hat and the old fur coat that was too long by several inches for the style of that year, she remembered how she had first come on the train herself, a girl with a yellow dress basket, and how much she had wanted Cartwright to meet her.

No one had spoken to her that day as she walked up the High Street between the closed shops, in the rain, and now no one spoke to her to-day as she walked to the station in the snow. Fresh snow had fallen in the night and lay to a depth of three or four inches, light and pure, on the roofs. It was churned to dark ribbons of ice-slush in the High Street and padded black by feet on the pavement ; but in the side streets and in the gardens of the houses and finally on the railway track itself it lay clean and untouched and pure too. The reflection of it was cast up into her face as she walked, her head bent slightly, so that her face looked dead white and frozen itself, her eyes like frosted glass. She had always been frightened of falling on the snow and she had put on a pair of big black goloshes that were a little too large for her. They made a slopping sound as she walked in the snow.

At the station no one but herself was waiting for the train. She did not feel very much as she stood there. It was cold to her feet and for a time she walked about and then finally she walked up and stood on the footbridge. Looking down the tracks she felt exactly the cold emptiness she saw there. The thin steel lines curved away on the pure white ground of snow and seemed to meet on the bare horizon. Her life seemed destined somehow to be bound up with the idiotic little train. When she had first come in by it she had felt proud and aloof and very sure : very sure of herself and Cartwright, very sure she was the one and only Miss Cassell, very sure of what she wanted. Now she did not feel sure of herself, and what she wanted was so simple that it was quite ridiculous. It was like expecting the two railway lines actually to converge and become one at a given point ; whereas you knew that they never could, never did and never would come the slightest fraction nearer to each other. Up the track the train would be coming in backwards ; in the train were two people. She did not know one of them much ; she did not know the other one at all. It was very ridiculous that it should make her feel as if her heart were broken up.

She ran one finger of her glove along the iron rim of the bridge. A little snow stuck to her glove and a little shower of it fell from the bridge. From the far side of the bridge three small boys ran up the steps and over the top and down the other side, laughing. They said something about the old woman but she did not hear it. At that moment the door of the station master's office banged and the station master came out on to the platform, stamping his feet in the snow, with a porter. There was very little luggage on the platform and no crates of pigeons. A moment or two later she saw the white smoke of the approaching train.

She stood there without moving as the train came in : three coaches, and the engine, as always, behind. It did not halt for more than a few moments. Looking down from the bridge she saw the young man from Warren Street get out of the train. He was carrying two suit-cases, and with him was the young woman. Mrs Cartwright saw the young woman look up. She looked rather excited and she smiled. It might have been herself arriving thirty years ago, looking up and getting her first sight of Evensford : except that there had then been no smile, no excitement and no one to meet her.

The train began to move out again, and a few moments later the platform was empty. She walked down from the bridge and round to the front of the station. She was just in time to see the man from Warren Street putting the two suit-cases into the only taxi that met the trains at Evensford, and to hear him say, 'Oh, it's cold and miserable. Better to ride.' She heard the sound of the young woman's voice laughing in reply and then the crackling sound of the taxi wheels in the crisp air as they moved over the frozen snow. As she watched the taxi disappear, leaving the short street empty, she knew suddenly how simple the solution to everything was : to be loved and to be wanted, to want someone and be wanted, ever so little, in return. She was struck again by the awful force of little things : a taxi on a cold day in the snow, an empty street in a strange town in the rain.

She walked heavily down the street in the snow. She stared at her feet, absurdly floppy in the goloshes that were too big for them. Her face was practically hidden by the big untidy scarf and there were patches of snow on the fur coat where she had leaned against the bridge.

The three small boys who had run over the bridge waited for her as she came down the street. They crouched down by the station wall, pressing snow-balls in their hands, and they had another pile of snow-balls already made, on the ground. In the reflected light of the snow their faces were shining with excitement.

As she came within range, not seeing them, looking down at her feet, walking as if she did not know where she was going, they pressed the snow-balls harder in their hands, laughing now.

'Get ready,' they said. 'Here she comes.'

EDITH McGILLCUDDY

JOHN STEINBECK

Salinas was a dirty little California cow-town in 1879. There was a small and consistent vicious element ; there was a large wavering element, likely to join the vicious element on Saturday night and go to church repentant on Sunday. And there was a small embattled good element, temperance people, stern people.

Twenty saloons kept the town in ignorance and vice while five churches fought valiantly for devotion, temperance, and decency.

The McGillcuddys belonged by right, by race, and by inclination to the good element. Mr McGillcuddy passed the plate in the Methodist church ; for the McGillcuddy family had joined the Methodists at a time when anyone who wasn't a Presbyterian was automatically an atheist or an idolator. Mrs McGillcuddy laboured at making the trousers that were sent twice a year to Africa and to the Sandwich Islands to curb the immorality of those backward peoples.

The little twelve-year-old Edith McGillcuddy, however, was a problem. Born to the good element, her instincts were bad in the matter of the company she kept. She could and did play decorously with the children of her own class but, left to her own devices, she invariably drifted to those dirty-faced children who, if they went to Sunday school at all, worshipped sticks and stones in the basement of the Catholic church. This was a matter of alarm and sometimes of anger to Mr and Mrs McGillcuddy.

One Sunday morning in summer, when the sunshine lay sweetly on the weedy lots and when the sloughs on the edge of town sent up an arrogant smell of moss and frogs and tules, Edith was given five cents and started on her way to Sunday school.

She had no intention of going anywhere else. Of course she rattled a stick against the fence pickets as she went along, but it was a small clean stick. She walked carefully to keep dust from flying on her blackinged shoes, and she didn't climb a fence and cut across lots because by so doing she might have torn her long black stockings. She brought her blonde braid round in front every now and then to see that the pink hair ribbon was stiff and perfect.

Had she climbed the fence none of this adventure would have happened. She walked around it instead and, at the corner, sitting among the mallow weeds, was Susy Nugger, a little girl of Edith's age but not of her class. Susy's hair strung down over her eyes like the forelock of a pony. Her face was sticky and streaked where candy juice had collected dust ; one puffed cheek was tight-stretched over a black all-day sucker. Her gingham dress was grey with dirt and she wore neither shoes nor stockings. Susy reclined among the yellowing mallow weeds and looked at the light summer sky. Occasionally she removed the sucker to see how it was getting along.

Edith didn't see Susy until she came abreast and until Susy spoke. 'Where you going ?'

Edith knew she shouldn't stop, but she did. 'Going to Sunday school. What you doing ?'

'Sucking on a sucker, and I bet you wish you had one,' said Susy. Her words were mushy because of the sucker. The two girls eyed each other belligerently.

'Well, I guess you better go on,' said Susy. 'I'm going to a free funeral.' She watched with satisfaction the interest rising in Edith's face, and she saw with malice that Edith was unconsciously picking her hair ribbon.

'What's a free funeral ?' Edith demanded. 'They're all free. They don't even pass the plate at funerals. I been to lots of them."

Susy plucked some little cheeses from the mallow weeds and put them in her mouth on top of the sucker. 'I bet you never went to a funeral that had a free train ride to it.'

Edith's hair ribbon suffered. 'Train ride to where ?'

'To Monterey, that's where, and back too. And it don't cost a cent to mourners or friends of the deceased.'

'I bet you aren't a mourner or a friend,' said Edith.

Susy took the paling sucker from her mouth and regarded it maddeningly. 'Well, if I cry a little ever'body'll think I am.'

Edith scuffed one toe in the dirt, forgetting the new blacking. 'Whyn't you come along?' Susy suggested.

'No. I got to go to Sunday school. Got the nickel for the plate right here.'

'Whyn't you wait till next Sunday and put two nickels in. They don't care just as long as they get it sometime.'

'God might not like it,' said the weakening Edith.

Susy guilefully pressed on. Nice-people she might not be, but logician she was. 'When you pray for something do you get it right off? No, sometimes you wait a long time for it and sometimes you don't get it at all. I prayed for about a million things and I never even got a smell of them. Why'nt you let God wait a week for his nickel?'

This was wrong, and Edith knew it was terribly wrong, but Susy was powerful and subtle. Out of her gingham pocket she drew a huge all-day sucker, scarlet and shiny. 'I was saving this red one for the funeral. It's a hot one.'

Edith gave up. 'The red ones always are hot,' she said kindly.

'Well, this one is the hottest you ever had. I tasted it. It'll burn the mouth right out of you. I ate the black one first because I like the red ones best, but you can have it.'

Edith accepted the sucker and the bribe. 'What train we going on, the big train?'

'Of course not,' said Susy. 'We're going on the narragauge. Not just one car either. The Alvarez family rented the whole train. They're going to bury 'Tonio Alvarez in Monterey.'

Before she put the big sucker in her mouth Edith rubbed it a little on her sleeve to prove she was still dainty. 'I guess we better be going to the depot and get a seat,' she said.

The funeral train was festive in a mournful kind of way. First was the little engine rolling black smoke out of its head and puffing steam out of its belly. After that was the flat car carrying the coffin on two saw-horses. Flowers and pillow pieces were piled all over the coffin car and no one sat on it. After that came four more flat cars with benches for the mourners. Black crepe hung from the funnel of the engine and lined the sides of the cars. By special arrangement with the company the train bell tolled mournfully.

Edith and Susy got there just in time. The coffin was in

place and the benches were nearly full of mourners. On the first two cars ladies and gentlemen in black formal clothes sat stiffly, ready handkerchiefs and smelling salts clutched in their hands. They had already got the churching over with. The priest and the family sat on the first car.

The last two cars were crowded with less formal people and the aisles between the benches were cluttered with lunch baskets and paper bags and cans of milk. Edith saw with relief that she and Susy were not the only ones who were combining a funeral and a free train ride. For there were courting couples whose self-imposed gravity was constantly racked with giggles. There were hair-trigger children who needed only a leader or an incident to break into happy riot.

The engine bell tolled mournfully on and the steam from the stomach of the engine hissed. Susy and Edith squeezed in and sat on the floor between two rows of benches. Already Edith's face was streaked with red from the sucker ; her hair ribbon was a ruin, and in crawling up on the flat car she had torn the knee out of one of her long ribbed stockings.

There came a pause to the tolling bell. Then the whistle screamed. The wheels turned and the little train gathered speed. It moved out of town and into the yellow grain fields. The wind rushed by. Some of the smaller bunches of flowers arose into the air and sailed away into the hayfields. Women gathered their dresses about their ankles and pinned their veils tight round their throats. The priest hugged his surplice close. Two boys were fighting already on the last car.

Through the ripening country the train tore at twenty miles an hour. The sparrow-hawks flew up from the squirrel holes and the blackbirds soared away in flocks, like wind-blown black curtains. The wind was warm and it was perfumed with the funeral flowers and with the black smoke from the engine. The sun shone brilliantly down ; the little train raced on through the hayfields.

Now a few people, made hungry by all the excitement, began to open the lunch baskets. Ladies pushed their veils up to take each bite of sandwich. The children in the last car threw orange peels and apple cores at one another.

The train left the yellow fields and entered the bleak country where the earth is dark sand and where even the sagebrush grows small and black. And then the round, sparkling bosom of Monterey Bay came into sight.

All this time the train bell tolled. Four men had climbed forward to the coffin car to hold down the larger and more expensive bunches of flowers and the symbolic funeral pieces, such as pillows and flower crosses and broadsides of red geraniums with lambs in white verbenas. A group of small boys on the last car began to snatch caps and throw them from the train.

It is remarkable that during the whole trip no one fell off the train. Nervous mothers spoke of it afterward, spoke of it as a provision of Providence, probably set in motion by the sacred nature of the journey. Not only did no one fall off, but no one was hurt in any way. When the train pulled into the depot at Monterey every passenger was safe. Ladies' clothes were a bit blown, but since their dresses were black they didn't show the engine smoke at all.

At the station in Monterey a crowd was waiting, for Monterey was the home seat of the Alvarez family, and the big granite tomb was in the Monterey cemetery. A hearse was waiting and a few surreys for the immediate family. The rest of the people formed in a long line to walk to the graveyard.

Just as they were about to move, the brakeman shouted, 'The train will start back at four o'clock, and it won't wait for nothing.'

THE GRANITE VAULT was open, its bronze doors wide. The crowd of people stood in a big half circle facing the entrance, and the coffin was in front of the door. The people had put their lunch baskets behind tombstones, out of the hot sun. Edith was alone now, for the treacherous Susy had allied herself with a little girl who carried a big lunch pail. Edith had seen them walking in the procession, Susy helping to carry the pail.

And now the grave service was going on, and Edith stood between two big men. She could see the inside of the vault with the inscribed squares where other coffins lay. She felt deserted and alone. The priest said the hollow burial service. Edith began to sniffle, her eyes dripped—suddenly she sobbed aloud.

One of the big men looked down at her. 'Who is this?' he asked of the big man on the other side. 'I don't recognise her.'

The other man glanced down at her and shrugged his

shoulders. 'One of 'Tonio's bastards, I guess. The country's full of them.'

Edith stopped crying. She didn't know what a bastard was, but she was glad to be one if it gave her an official position at the funeral. She watched while the coffin was carried into the vault and slid into the little black cave that was ready for it. Then the tomb door clanged shut and the people began to disperse, some to eat their lunches in the cemetery and others to search out the shade of oak trees on the hill behind the graveyard.

The crickets were singing in the tall grass and the bay breeze blew in over the graves. Edith looked for Susy and found her with her new friend. They were sitting on a cement slab eating thick sandwiches.

Susy called out ungraciously, 'Go away ! There's just enough for Ella and me, huh, Ella ? Ella's my friend. Huh, Ella ? Ella knows me.'

Edith turned disconsolately away. A reasonably well-fed McGillcuddy wouldn't think of eating thick sandwiches with Susys and Ellas, but Edith was growing hungry. Her insides were hollow too from the dry scanty wind. Nearly all the people were gone. Edith noticed that the wind brought with it a delicious odour. There was kelp in it and crabs and salt and clean damp sand ; but it was a lonely smell too. As Edith walked down toward the bay she thought of Salinas. Were her people looking for her body down wells or in the quicksand holes of the Salinas River ? For her family probably thought Edith was dead. Her eyes dampened. She thought how it would be to be dead, not in a dry, comfortable coffin like 'Tonio Alvarez, but floating in the stale water of an old well, or far down under the oozy quicksand. She felt very sad as she walked through the sunny streets until she came to the beach.

The little waves were lipping on the sand. A few rowboats lay bottom up on the beach. A wavy line of dead seaweeds left by the high tide cut the white beach in half. Edith walked thoughtfully to one of the overturned boats and sat down on it.

There came a scrabbling sound from under the boat. Edith got down on her knees and looked underneath. She leaped back quickly, for a dirty little face was peering out at her. The face and a frowsy, frizzled head came worming out from under the boat, and a red dress followed, and long, skinny bare legs. It was a plain ragamuffin. Compared to this little girl, Susy was as elevated as Edith was above Susy ; for this little spectre of dirt and low-classness not only had a dirty face and uncombed hair ; what was infinitely worse, she had on no pants under the dress, and she had not wiped her nose for a long time. She was on her knees now, clear of the boat, and she stared at Edith with animal eyes.

'What you doing under that boat ?' Edith demanded.

The ragamuffin spoke in a hoarse, cracked voice. 'Nothing. I was just laying there. What's it your business ?'

'What's your name ?' Edith continued sternly. Her tone cowed the wild girl.

'Name's Lizzie. And I never seen you before neither.'

'Of course you didn't. I came to the funeral from Salinas.'

'Oh ! That old funeral. I could of went to that. But I didn't want to.'

'Sure, you could of walked to it,' Edith agreed sarcastically, 'but you couldn't of come over to it from Salinas on a train.'

The shot was deep. Lizzie changed the subject. 'There's a lady in this town smokes cigarettes.'

'I don't believe it,' Edith said coldly.

A look of jeering triumph came on Lizzie's face. 'Ho ! You don't believe it, Miss Smarty-face. Well, I can show her to you with a cigarette right in her mouth.'

'I don't believe it,' Edith said again, but there was no conviction in her tone. She knew of course that it was impossible, but Lizzie's manner wavered the impossibility.

'You can come with me and I'll show you,'' Lizzie continued. 'And we can make a nickel too.'

'How ?''

'Well, this lady that smokes and a man with long hair live up to the Frenchman's. They buy ever'thing. They bought abalone shells even, and they could of picked up all they wanted. Everbody sells things to 'em. I bet they'd even buy dirt for a nickel. They aren't sharp ; that's what my pa says.'

'What are we going to sell them ?' Edith asked.

'Huckleb'rries,' said Lizzie. 'You come with me to Huckleb'rry Hill and help pick a bucket of berries, and we'll take them down, and the man with long hair'll give us a nickel for them, and you can see the lady smoking.'

'Is the man with long hair an Indian?'

'I don't think so. He's just kind of crazy. That's what my pa says.'

'Is he scary?'

'No, he ain't scary. He treats you nice and gives you a nickel for ever'thing.'

A warmth of yellow was in the afternoon sun as the two little girls climbed the hill among the tall straight pines. The straight shadows lay on the needle beds, and the little crisp dead pine twigs snapped under the girls' feet. Fallen pine cones littered the ground. Lizzie showed Edith how to bruise the Yerba Buena under the heel so that the sweet smell of it arose into the air. They tore their way through a blackberry thicket and the thorns didn't hurt Lizzie's bare feet. At last they came to the open slope where the neat huckleberry bushes grew, and the tips of the twigs were loaded with black fruit and the leaves of the bushes were as shiny as mirrors.

'There,' said Lizzie. 'Now we'll pick them. Don't mind if you get leaves in the bucket because those people will buy anything.'

Edith watched while her new friend filled half the bucket with pure huckleberry leaves. That helped to make the bucket fill up with berries more quickly. It took very little time to make the top brim with the black, shiny berries. The girls' hands were purple-black with the fruit juice.

The sun was even yellower when they went back down the hill and the wind came swishing up from the bay. The little fishing boats with sails were spanking home in the afternoon.

'Suppose they aren't home?' Edith suggested. 'The train's going back to Salinas at four o'clock.'

'Don't you worry. They'll be sitting right out in the yard on the ground, and the lady'll be smoking.'

They trudged through the dirt streets of Monterey. A few horsemen idled about and a few rigs were tied to the sidewalk hitching posts. A barouche passed, bearing a sad lady in black satin, and the polished spokes of the wheels flittered in the sunshine. At last Edith and Lizzie came to a large white adobe house. There were two storeys to the house and the curtains were red. Beside the house there was a high wall of limestones set in mud. Little eaves perched on top of the wall to keep the rain from washing the mud away. A heavy two-leaved gate was in the wall, and in the middle of the gate was a big iron ring. Over the wall the tops of fresh green trees showed and the tips of ivy.

Lizzie whispered hoarsely, 'They'll be sitting right on the ground. They always are.'

'On the ground ? No chairs ?'

'Right hell on the ground,' said Lizzie emphatically, 'and a tablecloth on the ground too.'

'I don't believe it,' said Edith.

'Well, you watch then.'

Lizzie picked up a stone from the ground and hammered on the gate. A sharp voice called, 'Pull on the ring if you want to get in.' Lizzie reached and gave the ring a tug.

The gate posts must have leaned inward, but without help, the heavy leaves folded open by themselves. Edith's eyes widened ; her mouth dropped open ; her hands hid in the folds of her ruined dress. It was just as Lizzie had said it would be. The yard was flagged with smooth limestones. Nice trees lined the walls. Toward the back of the yard a white cloth was on the ground and a teapot and cups. On one side of the cloth sat a lady in a white dress smoking a cigarette, and on the other side squatted a long-haired young man with a lean, sick face and eyes shining with fever. A smile came on the young man's face, but the lady did not change her expression ; she just looked blankly at the two little girls standing in the open gateway. Edith and Lizzie stood self-conscious and clumsy. When the young man spoke, some kind of a memory rippled in Edith's head.

'What is it you want, girls ?'

Lizzie's hoarse, cracked voice came explosively. 'Huckle-b'rries,' she croaked. 'Nice fresh huckleb'rries. Fi' cents a bucket.'

The young man put a lean hand in his pocket and brought out a coin. Edith and Lizzie marched stiffly forward. Lizzie held out the bucket of berries and took the coin in her purple paw. Then, without warning, she whirled and ran like a rabbit out the gate. It was so silent in the yard that Edith could hear the retreating footsteps for a time after the disappearance of her friend.

Edith turned slowly to the people. The lady's face had not changed. A little spurt of smoke escaped from her nose and writhed in her dark hair. The young man smiled ruefully. 'She did you, didn't she ?' he observed.

Then Edith's anger arose. 'That's not all,' she said sharply. 'The bucket's more than half leaves.'

The long-haired man smiled on. 'It always is,' he said gently. 'One must take that into consideration.'

'You knew it ?' Edith demanded.

'Oh ! Gracious, yes. But,' he said softly, 'I didn't care.'

The woman on the other side of the cloth spoke for the first time. 'They just take you for a fool. They make a fool of you.'

The man pinched the tip of his nose. 'It's not bad sport to be a fool,' he said, '—for five cents.' He faced Edith again. 'Will you have a cup of tea ?'

She looked yearningly at the fat brown teapot on the ground and at the fat brown sugar bowl and cream pitcher. 'I'm not allowed to have tea. My mother won't let me."

The man bowed in the face of this law.

Edith continued quickly, 'But if it's half milk, that's cambric tea.'

'Certainly it is,' he said sharply. 'Certainly it is.'

'And I can have that.'

He poured it for her and held out the brown sugar bowl. Edith sat down on the ground. The woman still gazed at her, but Edith's courage came back. Edith was what she was. 'You aren't an Indian, I guess,' she observed.

'No. I'm really not.'

'Because,' she went on, 'you talk pretty near like Granma McGillcuddy.'

'You have a Grandma McGillcuddy ?' the young man cried.

'My own name is Edith McGillcuddy and I live in Salinas and I came on a train to the free funeral. . . .'

The man turned to the woman. 'Take note of this,' he said happily. 'There is more in a line than I could do. There's condensation for you, and history, and if you were so minded—philosophy.'

The woman looked slightly annoyed.

Edith sipped her cambric tea and continued, 'I should have gone to Sunday school.'

'You should, all right,' agreed the man. 'Salinas is twenty miles away, isn't it ?'

'Yes, and it's a nice town, but there's no ocean beside it and it's got twenty saloons.' Edith nodded dismally to show how bad the last fact was.

'The McGillcuddys of Salinas,' he murmured, 'and you came in a train to the free—look, what's a free funeral ?'

At that moment a high scream filled the air. Edith grew tense. The scream was repeated. 'I know,' she cried. 'It's the train going back.' She ran wildly out through the big gates and kited down the hill. The train was just beginning to move when she climbed aboard.

And that was how Edith McGillcuddy met Robert Louis Stevenson.

IN THE TRAIN

DILYS POWELL

London's broken walls and static water lay clear under the bright night as the train swung through the suburbs, threw out its chest and sprang ferociously westward, flaunting its fiery sheaf of smoke and sparks. The passengers squirmed uneasily and composed themselves for night and silence : the young Jew, up for the fight, impassively resigned himself to the long return journey in the corridor, the optimist with no luggage but a deck chair accepted without rancour his ejection from the luggage van. There was not room for a mouse. In the dark carriages people slept sitting upright with lolling heads, or swung like gibbons from the luggage racks and stared out at the moonflushed sky and black fleeting trees. Soldiers and airmen, squatting in the corridors, leaned against one another in bunches, like carelessly stacked rifles. Even the ticket-collector's cubby-hole was occupied. 'May be a war on,' the ticket-collector complained, 'but I still don't want nobody watching me eat my bit of supper.' It was not until Swindon that the man from the Ministry of Supply scurried down the platform, running awkwardly with his luggage, and found a seat in a first class carriage.

The shaded lamps shed not so much light as cones of illumined fog on the sleeping carriage. The Civil Servant groped in the rack, found a space for his suitcase, and sat down stealthily, wondering if he could risk eating his sandwiches without waking anyone. He took a look round. In the corner on his right the pallid cone picked out the tired young face of a man in naval uniform; there were wings above the braid on his sleeve. A Merchant Navy officer, still ruddy from the salty breath of the sea, slumped and slept opposite; next to him a blonde girl in tweeds twisted restlessly, leaning her head first on one hand, then on the other. On his left the Civil Servant made out a check riding coat and two old, twisted hands resting on the knees of a pair of jodhpurs; opposite, a nondescript figure in an overcoat. Cautious as a pickpocket, the Civil Servant unscrewed his thermos.

Suddenly a voice spoke on his right.

'I see you've brought the right book with you.'

The Civil Servant glanced down at the book on his lap. It was *The Worst Journey in the World*. Then he smiled at the Lieutenant and nodded without speaking.

'Been standing in the corridor?' said the Lieutenant, levering himself up in his corner.

'Yes,' said the Civil Servant, looking at the sleeping passengers and speaking softly. 'Have you?'

'Oh, yes. This is my fifth night without going to bed,' said the Lieutenant in a clear unhushed voice.

'Duty or pleasure?' said the Civil Servant, still softly.

'Well, both,' said the Lieutenant. The Merchant Navy officer stirred, smacked his lips twice, and began to snore. The Lieutenant looked at him with disapproval, as if half-inclined to ask him to be quiet and let other people hear themselves speak, then went on loudly, 'Had a bit of a night last night. Of course, I'm used to not sleeping.'

On the other side of the Civil Servant a small old face, beaked like the Duke of Wellington's, thrust out above the check coat, yawned, blinked under the shaded lamp and spoke to nobody in particular.

'Tired out I am. Standing up in the van like horses we were, just like horses, only nowhere near so sensible.'

'Going far?' said the Civil Servant, giving up the attempt to whisper.

'A tidy way,' said the old man. 'I made up my mind to see the Dartmoor ponies. I knew I had to have a holiday. Going to bed tired I was and getting up tired. I knew I had to have a holiday. So I thought I might as well go and see the Dartmoor ponies. Heard a lot about them, but never seen them, I haven't.'

The figure opposite him shuffled, huddled deeper in its overcoat, and turned resignedly to the blind face of the window. The Merchant Navy officer, safe from the sea, snored on.

' 'Twould pay me,' said the old man, 'to buy six or seven Dartmoor ponies. I could break them in in three months and sell them for children. Do nicely they would for children's mounts.'

'Much riding going on in wartime ?' said the Civil Servant.

'Oh, yes,' said the old man, 'I teach a lot of children riding. I've got a big school. I used to be a jockey, when I was a bit younger, you know. Lord Epsom's children, they all come to me. Lord Epsom, he wouldn't let them go to nobody else. There's little Susan now, sits her pony as cool as a knife. Shamrock, that's the pony she rides. Eh, there's a good pony. Understands every word you say, every word. "Go on now, Shamrock," I say to her, "Go on, Shamrock," I say, and off she goes. Jump a stone fence, she will.'

The train clanked slowly into a station and stood hissing softly. In the next compartment a spring creaked, a voice complained, then silence. High in the night a plane sang its waspish song.

'This train travel gets me down,' said the Lieutenant. 'I've been travelling since yesterday morning. Give me a plane and I could do it in twenty minutes.'

'Tired ?' said the Civil Servant, yawning hopefully.

'Lord, no,' said the Lieutenant. 'Haven't had more than a couple of hours' sleep together in a night for the last six months. You get used to it.'

Footsteps grated in the mysterious world beyond the windows. A whistle blew, remote and shrill. The train jolted, sending small clanking shudders down its length, heaved slowly forward, then flung itself passionately in the direction of Plymouth.

'Enjoy flying ?' said the Civil Servant, thinking, not without envy, of the hard life of action and danger.

'Oh, yes,' said the Lieutenant. Beneath his casual manner he

o

was confident and aware of his responsibilities. 'Nice to come south again though.'

'Been far north?' said the Civil Servant.

'Mm,' said the Lieutenant. 'Funny, you know, up there you get all sorts of odd things. Compass, for instance. Can't use it sometimes.' He began to talk of the Fleet Air Arm, of magnetic aberrations, sea patrols, improved bomb sights. 'Be dropping them in their hip-pockets soon,' he said.

Listening, the Civil Servant thought of the clouds, the winds, the cold sea. 'Before the war,' he said, 'were you——'

'Oh,' said the Lieutenant, 'you get around. I rode all over the place in the Argentine once. I've got French blood,' he added, as if in extenuation. 'I know the States pretty well, too . . . American girls. Plenty of life. Like tomboys, you know. Ride, swim, beat you in the hundred yards. Perfectly wizard they are. No self-consciousness or anything like that.'

'I often think,' said the Civil Servant, 'it's because German women are so plain that the Germans are always wanting to make war. They've got nothing else to occupy their minds.'

'You've got something there,' said the Lieutenant. 'Of course, English girls . . . I mean, it seems to me, why don't we have some kind of sex education?'

'There's some people,' interrupted the old man violently, 'talks a lot about training ponies by kindness. "Talk to 'em," they say, "persuade 'em to trust you." ' His old voice, throaty, with its rustic vowels, took on a note of scorn. 'What would I be doing persuading ponies? I haven't the time, I haven't the time! If I can buy six or seven Dartmoor ponies, why, I'll break them in in three months.'

The blonde opposite breathed deeply in the shadow and turned to rest her head on the other hand.

'I'd put them to dragging things, gradually,' said the old man, 'a log maybe, or an old motor tyre. Then something on their backs—oh, they go off like wildfire at first, galloping and galloping, but they soon get tired. Why, in three months I can sell them for children.'

'As I was saying,' said the Lieutenant, 'English girls. Lots of them grow up . . . I mean, it's pretty silly——'

The blonde, keeping her eyes shut, took her hand from her ear and turned once more in the direction of the voice.

'Don't get a look-in,' went on the Lieutenant. 'Of course, it's astonishing nowadays the girls who . . . Well, one day I was trying to find some club or other, somewhere in Mayfair. I rang the wrong bell, and a girl came to the door. I mean, you could have taken her anywhere. Smart, nice manners. We stood there talking. Lovely girl—dark. I mean, you could have taken her anywhere. "Won't you come in and have a drink?" she said. Strange. I still can't make it out. Oh, I just thanked her and whistled off.'

A wistful shade settled on the pale young face. The Civil Servant gave him a cigarette, then offered one to the old man.

'Thank you,' said the old man. 'They do say, God sent the horses, and the devil sent the riders. The Mowcher, now, there was a horse for you. Jump a stone wall, he would. Three times I sold him and bought him back. Understood every word you said. There was a book written about him. *The Mowcher*, it was called.'

The single roar of the flying wheels broke into a distinguishable rhythm, slower, slower, then stopped. Silence. The Merchant Navy officer woke up, looked about him with a sour, bewildered air, and closed his eyes again. Silence. A shriek far away resolved itself into the monotonous rattle of passing goods trucks.

'I've heard,' said the old man as the train moved on, 'those Dartmoor ponies do make nice riding ponies. I shall buy six or seven of them, if I can find a farmer to sell. I shall get a truck to take them back. 'Twill be nicer for them, they can look out and see where they are.'

'The French,' said the Lieutenant, brightening, 'take a different view of life. Matter-of-fact, if you know what I mean. Of course, I've French blood myself. In Marseilles, for instance, you see the most extraordinary . . . Why, in some streets . . .'

Cautiously the girl took a peep, then hastily shut her eyes again.

'Tired?' said the Civil Servant again.

'No, after being up five nights,' said the Lieutenant, 'you begin to forget about sleep. I don't feel at all tired. Oh, well, not long now. Ten o'clock, and I shall be eating bacon and eggs at my sister's place and sizzling in the sun."

He stretched his long legs, exposing abbreviated flying-boots, yawned suddenly, and shut his eyes. He was asleep.

'That gentleman,' said the old man, 'reminds me of another gentleman used to ride with me, hunting. A fine rider he was. Jump a stone wall in cold blood, he would. I'm looking forward to seeing those Dartmoor ponies,' the old man went on gaily. 'I knew I had to have a holiday. Went to bed tired and got up tired I did.'

The Civil Servant leaned forward and pulled a blind aside. The world was new and bright, and the hurrying fields shone in the morning air. He looked at his watch. Seven o'clock. Seven o'clock on the morning of September 1. Three years of it, he thought with surprise ; and fell asleep. The day beamed through the carriage windows on the travellers with their unconquerable hopes and desires and curiosities : on the old riding-master, on the restless blonde, on the Lieutenant, youthful in sleep, on all the people whose lives lay, perhaps, in his flyer's hands. And the train, triumphant, plunged on past woods and hills, past streams, past meadows, past farms, past factories, flaunting its snowy plume of smoke like the challenge of the stubborn individuality of men to fear and death and the easy despair of the coward soul.

SERGEANT CARMICHAEL

FLYING OFFICER X

For some time he had had a feeling that none of them knew where they were going. They had flown over France without seeing the land. Now they were flying in heavy rain without a glimpse of the sea. He was very young, just twenty, and suddenly he had an uneasy idea that they would never see either the land or the sea again.

'Transmitter pretty U/S, sir,' he said.

For a moment there was no answer. Then Davidson, the captain, answered automatically, 'Keep trying, Johnny,' and he answered 'O.K.,' quite well knowing there was nothing more he could do. He sat staring straight before him. Momentarily he was no longer part of the aircraft. He was borne away from it on sound-waves of motors and wind and rain, and for a few minutes he was back in England, recalling and re-living odd moments of life there. He recalled for a second or two his first day on the station ; it was August and he remembered that some straw had blown in from the fields across the runways and that the wind of the take-offs whirled it madly upward, yellow and shining in the sun. He recalled his father eating red currants in the garden that same summer and how the crimson juice had spurted on to his moustache, so that he looked rather ferocious every time he said, 'That, if you want it, is my opinion.' And then he remembered, most curiously of all, a girl in a biscuit-yellow hat sitting in a deck-chair on the sea-front, eating a biscuit-yellow ice cream, and how he had been fascinated because hat and ice were miraculously identical in colour and how he had wanted to ask her, with nervous bravado because he was very young, if she bought her hats to match her ice-cream or her ice-cream to match her hats, but how he never did. He did not know why he recalled these moments, clear as glass, except perhaps that they were moments of a life he was never going to see again.

He was suddenly ejected out of this past world, fully alert and aware that they were not flying straight. They had not been flying straight for some time. They were stooging round and round, bumping heavily, and losing height. He sat very tense, and became gradually aware that this tension was part of the plane. It existed in each one of them from Davidson and Porter in the nose, down through Johnson and Hargreaves and himself to Carmichael, in the tail.

He heard Davidson's voice. 'How long since we had contact with base ?'

He looked at his watch ; it was almost midnight. 'A little under an hour and three-quarters,' he said.

Again there was silence ; and again he felt the tension running through the plane. He was aware of their chances and almost aware, now, of what Davidson was going to say.

'One more try, boys. Sing out if you see anything. If not it's down in the drink.'

He sat very still. They were losing a little height. His stomach felt sour and he remembered that he could not swim.

For some reason he never thought of it again. His thoughts were scattered by Davidson's voice.

'Does anyone see what I see ? Isn't that a light ? About two points to starboard.'

He looked out ; there was nothing he could see.

'I'm going down to have a look-see,' Davidson said. 'It *is* a light.'

As they were going down he looked out again, but again he could see nothing. Then he heard Davidson speaking to Carmichael.

'Hack the fuselage door off, Joe. This looks like a lightship. If it is we're as good as home. Tell me when you're ready and I'll put her down.'

He sat very still, hearing the sound of hatchet blows as Carmichael struck at the fuselage. He felt suddenly colder, and then knew that it must be because Carmichael had finished and that there was a gap where the door had been. He heard again the deep slow Canadian accent of Carmichael's voice, saying, 'O.K., skipper, all set,' and then the remote flat English voice of Davidson in reply :

'All right, get the dinghy ready. All three of you. Get ready and heave it out when I put her down.'

Helping Joe and Hargreaves and Johnson with the dinghy he was no longer aware of fear. He was slung sideways across the aircraft. There was not much room. The dinghy seemed very large and he wondered how they would get it out. This troubled him until he felt the plane roaring down in the darkness, and it continued to trouble him for a second after the plane had hit the water with a great crash that knocked him back against the fuselage. He did not remember getting up. Something was wrong with his left wrist, and he thought of his watch. It was a good watch, a navigational watch, given him by his father on a birthday. The next moment he knew that the dinghy had gone and he knew that he had helped, somehow, to push it out. Carmichael had also gone. The sea was rocking the aircraft violently to and fro, breaking water against his knees and feet. A second later he stretched out his hands and felt nothing before him but the open space in the fuselage where the door had been.

He knew then that it must be his turn to go. He heard Carmichael's voice calling from what seemed a great distance out of the darkness and the rain. He did not know what he was calling. It was all confused, he did not answer, but a second later he stretched out his hands blindly and went down on his belly in the sea.

2

WHEN HE CAME UP again it was to find himself thinking of the girl in the biscuit-coloured hat and how much, that day, he had liked the sea, opaque and green and smooth as the pieces of sea-washed glass he had picked up on the shore. It flashed through his mind that this was part of the final imagery that comes with drowning, and he struggled wildly to keep his face above water. He could hear again the voice of Carmichael, shouting, but the shock of sea water struck like ice on his breast and throat, so that he could not shout in answer. The sea was very rough. It heaved him upwards and then down again with sweeps of slow and violent motion. It tossed him about in this way until he realised at last that these slow, barbaric waves were really keeping him up, that the Mac West was working and that he was sinking away no longer.

From the constancy of Carmichael's shouts he felt that Carmichael must have seized, and was probably on, the dinghy. But he was not prepared for the shout : 'She's upside down !' and then a moment or two later two voices, yelling his name.

Johnny ! Can you hear us ? Can you hear us now ?'

He let out a great yell in answer but sea water broke down his throat, for a moment suffocated him, bearing him down and under the trough of a wave. He came up sick and struggling, spitting water, frightened. His boots were very heavy now under the water and it seemed as if he were being sucked continually down. He tried to wave his arms above his head but one arm had no response. It filled him suddenly with violent pain.

'O.K., Johnny, O.K., O.K.,' Carmichael said.

He could not speak. He knew that his arm was broken. He felt Carmichael's hands painfully clutching his one free hand. He remembered for no reason at all that Carmichael had been a pitcher for a baseball team in Montreal, and he felt the hands move down until they clutched his wrist, holding him so strongly that it was almost a pain.

'Can you bear up ?' Carmichael said. 'Johnny, try bearing

up. It's O.K., Johnny. We're here, on the dinghy. Hargreaves is here. Johnson's here. We're all here except the skipper. It's O.K., Johnny. Can you heave ? Where's your other arm ?'

'I think it's bust,' he said.

He tried heaving himself upward. He tried again, helped by Carmichael's hands, but something each time drew the dinghy away. He tried again and then again. Each time the same thing happened, and once or twice the sea, breaking on the dinghy, hit him in the face, blinding him.

He knew suddenly what was wrong. It was not only his arm but his belt. Each time he heaved upward the belt caught under the dinghy and pushed it away. In spite of knowing it he heaved again and all at once felt very tired, feeling that only Carmichael's hands were between this tiredness and instant surrender. This painful heaving and sudden tiredness were repeated. They went on for some time. He heard Carmichael's voice continually and once or twice the sea hit him again, blinding him, and once, blinded badly, he wanted to wipe his face with his hands.

Suddenly Carmichael was talking again. 'Can you hang on ? If I can get my knee on something I'll get leverage. I'll pull you up. Can you hang on ?'

Before he could answer the sea hit him again. The waves seemed to split his contact with Carmichael. It momentarily cut away his hands. For an instant it was as if he were in a bad and terrifying dream, falling through space.

Then Carmichael was holding him again. 'I got you now Johnny. I'm kneeling on Dicky. Your belt ought to clear now. If you try hard it ought to clear first time.'

The sea swung him away. As he came back the belt did not hit the dinghy so violently. He was kept almost clear. Then the sea swung him away again. On this sudden wave of buoyancy he realised that it was now, or perhaps never, that he must pull himself back. He clenched his hand violently ; and then suddenly before he was ready, and very lightly as if he were a child, the force of the new wave and the strength of Carmichael's hands threw him on the dinghy, face down.

He wanted to lie there for a long time. He lay for only a second, and then got up. He felt the water heaving in his boots and the salt sickness of it in his stomach. He did not feel at all calm but was terrified for an instant by the shock of being safe.

'There was a light,' he said. 'That's why he came down here. That's why he came down. There was a light.'

He looked around at the sea as he spoke. Sea and darkness were one, unbroken except where waves struck the edge of the dinghy with spits of faintly phosphorescent foam. It had ceased raining now but the wind was very strong and cold, and up above lay the old unbroken ten-tenths cloud. There was not even a star that could have been mistaken for a light. He knew that perhaps there never had been.

He went into a slight stupor brought on by pain and the icy sea water. He came out of it to find himself furiously baling water from the dinghy with one hand. He noticed that the rest were baling with their caps. He had lost his cap. His one hand made a nerveless cup that might have been stone for all the feeling that was in it now.

The sea had a rhythmical and awful surge that threw the dinghy too lightly up the glassy arcs of oncoming waves and then too steeply over the crest into the trough beyond. Each time they came down into a trough the dinghy shipped a lot of water. Each time they baled frenziedly, sometimes throwing the water over each other. His good hand remained dead. He still did not feel the water with it but he felt it on his face, sharp as if the spray were splintered and frozen glass. Then whenever they came to the crest of a wave there was a split second when they could look for a light. 'Hell, there should be a light,' he thought. 'He saw one. He shouted it out. That's why he came down,' but each time the sea beyond the crest of the new wave remained utterly dark as before.

'What the hell,' he said. 'There should be a light ! There *was* a light.'

'All right, kid,' Carmichael said. 'There'll be one.'

He knew then that he was excited. He tried not to be excited. For a long time he didn't speak, but his mind remained excited. He felt drunk with the motion of pain and the water and sick with the saltness of the water. There were moments when he ceased baling and held his one hand strengthlessly at his side, tired out, wanting to give up. He did not know how he kept going after a time or how they kept the water from swamping the dinghy.

Coming out of periods of stupor, he would hear Carmichael talking. The deep Canadian voice was slow and steady. It attracted him. He found himself listening simply to the sound and the steadiness of it, regardless of words. It had the quality of Carmichael's hands ; it was calm and steadfast.

It occurred to him soon that the voice had another quality. It was like the baling of the water ; it never stopped. He heard Carmichael talking of ball games in Montreal ; the way the crowd ragged you and how you took no notice and how it was all part of the game ; and then how he was injured in the game one summer and for two months couldn't play and how he went up into Quebec province for the fishing. It was hot weather and he would fish mostly in the late evenings, often by moonlight. The lake trout were big and strong and sometimes a fish took you an hour to get in. Sometimes at week-ends he went back to Quebec and he would eat steaks as thick, he said, as a volume of Dickens and rich with onions and butter. They were lovely with cold light beer, and the whole thing set you back about two dollars and a half.

'Good, eh, Johnny ?' he would say. 'You ought to come over there some day.'

All the time they baled furiously. There was no break in the clouds and the wind was so strong that it sometimes swivelled the dinghy round like a toy.

How long this went on he did not know. But a long time later Carmichael suddenly stopped talking and then as suddenly began again.

'Hey, Johnny boy, there's your light !'

He was startled and he looked up wildly, not seeing anything.

'Not that way, boy. Back of you. Over there.'

He turned his head stiffly. There behind him he could see the dim cream edge of daylight above the line of the sea.

'That's the light we want,' Carmichael said. 'It don't go out in a hurry either.'

The colour of daylight was deeper, like pale butter, when he looked over his shoulder again. He remembered then that it was late summer. He thought that now, perhaps, it would be three o'clock.

As the daylight grew stronger, changing from cream and yellow to a cool grey bronze, he saw for the first time the barbaric quality of the sea. He saw the faces of Carmichael and Hargreaves and Johnson. They were grey-yellow with weariness and touched at the lips and ears and under the eyes with blue.

He was very thirsty. He could feel a thin caking of salt on his lips. He tried to lick his lips with his tongue but it was very painful. There was no moisture on his tongue and only the taste of salt, very harsh and bitter, in his mouth. His arm was swollen and he was sick with pain.

'Take it easy a minute, kid,' Carmichael said. 'We'll bale in turns. You watch out for a ship or a kite or anything you can see. I'll tell you when it's your turn.'

He sat on the edge of the dinghy and stared at the horizon and the sky. Both were empty. He rubbed the salt out of his eyes and then closed them for a moment, worn out.

'Watch out,' Carmichael said. 'We're in the Channel. We know that. There should be ships and there should be aircraft. Keep watching.'

He kept watching. His eyes were painful with salt and only half-open. Now and then the sea hit the dinghy and broke right over it, but he did not care. For some reason he did not think of listening, but suddenly he shut his eyes and after a moment or two he heard a sound. It was rather like the sound of the sea beating gently on sand, and he remembered again the day when he had seen the girl in the biscuit-coloured hat and how it was summer and how much he had liked the sea. That day the sea had beaten on the shore with the same low sound.

As the sound increased he suddenly opened his eyes. He felt for a moment that he was crazy, and then he began shouting.

'It's a plane ! It's a bloody plane ! It's a plane, I tell you, it's a plane !'

'Sit down,' Carmichael said.

The dinghy was rocking violently. The faces of all four men were upturned, grey-yellow in the stronger light.

'There she is !' he shouted. 'There she is !'

The plane was coming over from the north-east, at about five thousand. He began to wave his hands. She seemed to be coming straight above them. Hargreaves and Johnson and then Carmichael also began to wave. They all waved frantically and Hargreaves shouted, 'It's a Hudson, boys. Wave like raving Hallelujah ! It's a Hudson.'

The plane came over quite fast and very steady, flying straight. It looked the colour of iron except for the bright rings of the markings in the dull sea-light of the early morning. It flew on quite straight and they were still waving frantically with their hands and caps long after it had ceased looking like a far-off gull in the sky.

He came out of the shock of this disappointment to realise that Carmichael was holding him in the dinghy with one arm.

'I'm all right,' he said.

'I know,' Carmichael said.

He knew then that he was not all right. He felt dizzy. A slow river of cold sweat seemed to be pouring from his hair down his backbone.

'What happened?' he said.

'You're all right,' Carmichael said. 'Don't try to stand up again, that's all. How's your arm? I wish there was something I could do.'

' It's O.K.,' he said.

He remembered the plane. The sky was now quite light, barred with warm strips of orange low above the water in the east. He remembered also that it was summer. The wind was still strong and cold but soon, he thought, there will be sun. He looked overhead at the grey-blue and the yellow-orange bars of cloud. They were breaking a little more overhead and he knew now that it would be a fair day for flying.

'Does the sun rise in the east or a little to the north-east?' Carmichael said.

They held a little discussion, and Johnny and Hargreaves agreed that in summer it rose a little to the north-east.

'In that case we seem to be drifting almost due north. If the wind helps us we might drift into the coast. It's still strong.'

'It's about forty,' Hargreaves said. 'It must have been about eighty last night.'

'It was a point or two west of south then,' Johnny said.

'I think it's still there,' Carmichael said.

They all spoke rather slowly. His own lips felt huge and dry with blisters. It was painful for him to speak. He was not hungry, but the back of his throat was scorched and raw with salt. His tongue was thick and hot and he wanted to roll it out of his mouth, so that it would get sweet and cool in the wind.

'Keep your mouth shut, Johnny,' Carmichael said. 'Keep it shut.'

He discovered that Carmichael was still holding him by the

arm. In the hour or two that went by between the disappearance of the Hudson and the time when the sun was well up and he could feel the warmth of it on his face he continually wanted to protest ; to tell Carmichael that he was all right. Yet he never did and all the time Carmichael held him and he was glad.

All the time they watched the sea and the sky and most of the time Carmichael talked to them. He talked to them again of Canada, the lakes in the summertime, the fishing, the places where you could eat in Montreal. The sea was less violent now, but the waves, long and low and metallically glittering in the sun, swung the dinghy ceaselessly up and down troughs that bristled with destructive edges of foam. Towards the middle of the morning Hargreaves was very sick. He leaned his head forward on his knees and sat very quiet for a long time, too weak to lift his head. The sickness itself became covered and churned and finally washed away by incoming water. After this only Johnson and Carmichael troubled to watch the horizon, and they took turns at baling the water, Carmichael using one hand.

For some time none of them spoke. Finally when Johnny looked up again it was to see that Johnson too had closed his eyes against the glitter of sunlight and that only Carmichael was watching the sea. He was watching in a curious attitude. As he held Johnny with one hand he would lean forward and with his hat bale a little water out of the dinghy. Then he would transfer the hat from one hand to the other and with the free hand press the fabric of the dinghy as you press the inner tube of a tyre. As he pressed it seemed flabby. Then he would look up and gaze for a few moments at the horizon, northwards, where at intervals the sea seemed to crystallise into long lips of misty grey. For a long time Johnny sat watching him, following the movements of his hands and the arrested progress of his eyes.

Very slowly he realised what was happening. He did not move. He wanted to speak but the back of his throat was raw and his tongue was thick and inflexible. When he suddenly opened his mouth his lips split and there was blood in the cracks that was bitterly salt as he licked it with his tongue.

He did not know which struck him first : the realisation that the thin lips of grey on the horizon were land or that the dinghy was losing air. For a second or two his emotions were cancelled out. The dinghy was upside down ; the bellows were gone. He felt slightly light-headed. Above the horizon the clouds were white-edged now, and suddenly the sun broke down through them and shone on the line of land, turning the lips of grey to brown. He knew then that it was land. There could be no mistake. But looking down suddenly into the dinghy he knew that there was and could be no mistake there either.

He began to shout. He did not know what he shouted. His mouth was very painful. He rocked his body forward and began to bale excitedly with his free hand. In a moment the rest were shouting too.

'Steady,' Carmichael said, 'steady.'

'How far is it away?' Hargreaves said. 'Five miles? Five or six?'

'Nearer ten.'

'I'll take a bet.'

'You'd better take one on the air in the dinghy.'

It was clear that Hargreaves did not know about the air in the dinghy. He ceased baling and sat very tense. His tongue was thick and grey-pink and hanging out of his mouth.

It seemed to Johnny that the dinghy, slowly losing resilience, was like something dying underneath them.

'Now don't anybody go and get excited,' Carmichael said. 'We must be drifting in fast, and if we drift in far enough and she gives out we can swim. You all better bale now while you can. All right, Johnny? Can you bale?'

Baling frantically with his one hand, looking up at intervals at the horizon, now like a thin strip of cream brown paint squeezed along the edge of the sea, he tried not to think of the fact that he could not swim.

All the time he felt the dinghy losing air. He felt its flabbiness grow in proportion to his own weight. It moved very heavily and sluggishly in the troughs of water, and waves broke over it more often now. Sometimes the water rose almost to the knees of the men. He could not feel his feet and several times it seemed as if the bottom of the dinghy had fallen out and that beneath him there was nothing but the bottom of the sea.

It went on like this for a long time, the dinghy losing air, the land coming a little nearer, deeper coloured now, with veins of green.

'God, we'll never make it,' Hargreaves said. 'We'll never make it.'

Carmichael did not speak. The edge of the dinghy was low against the water, almost level. The sea lapped over it constantly and it was more now than they could bale.

Johnny looked at the land. The sun was shining down on smooth uplands of green and calm brown squares of upturned earth. Below lay long chalk cliffs, changing from sea-grey to white in the sun. He felt suddenly exhausted and desperate. He felt that he hated the sea. He was frightened of it and suddenly lost his head and began to bale with one arm, throwing the water madly everywhere.

'We'll never do it !' he shouted. 'We'll never do it. Why the hell didn't that Hudson see us ! What the hell do they do in those fancy kites !'

'Shut up,' Carmichael said.

He felt suddenly quiet and frightened.

'Shut up. She's too heavy, that's all. Take your boots off.'

Hargreaves and Johnson stopped baling and took off their boots. He tried to take off his own boots but they seemed part of his feet and with only one arm he was too weak to pull them off. Then Carmichael took off his own boots. He took off his socks too, and Johnny could see that Carmichael's feet were blue and dead.

For a minute he could not quite believe what he saw next. He saw Carmichael roll over the side of the dinghy into the sea. He went under and came up again at once, shaking the water from his hair. 'O.K.,' he shouted, 'O.K. Keep baling. I'm pushing her in. She'll be lighter now.'

Carmichael put his hands on the end of the dinghy and swam with his feet.

'I'm coming over too,' Hargreaves said.

'No. Keep baling. Keep her light. There'll be time to come over.'

They went on like this for some time. The situation in the dinghy was bad, but he did not think of it. His knees were sometimes wholly submerged and the dinghy was flabby and without life. All the time he hated the sea and kept his eyes in desperation on the shore. Then Carmichael gave Hargreaves the order to go over and Hargreaves rolled over the side as Carmichael had done and came up soon and began swimming in the same way.

They were then about five hundred yards from the shore and

he could see sheep in the fields above the cliffs, but no houses. The land looked washed and bright and for some reason abandoned, as if no one had ever set foot there. The sea was calm now, but it still washed over the dinghy too fast for him to bale and he still hated it. Then suddenly Johnson went over the side without waiting for a word from Carmichael, and he was alone in the dinghy, being pushed along by the three men. But he knew soon that it could not last. The dinghy was almost flat, and between the force of the three men pushing and the resistance of water it crumpled and submerged and would not move.

As if there were something funny about this Johnson began laughing. He himself felt foolish and scared and waited with clenched teeth for the dinghy to go down.

It went down before he was ready, throwing him backwards. He felt a wave hit him and then he went under, his boots dragging him down. He struggled violently and quite suddenly saw the sky. His arm was very painful and he felt lop-sided. He was lying on his back and he knew that he was moving, not of his own volition but easily and strongly, looking at the lakes of summer sky between the white and indigo hills of cloud. He was uneasy and glad at the same time. The sea still swamped over his face, scorching his broken lips, but he was glad because he knew that Carmichael was holding him again and taking him in to shore.

What seemed a long time later he knew that they were very near the shore. He heard the loud warm sound of breaking waves. He was borne forward in long surges of the tide. At last he could no longer feel Carmichael's arms, but tired and kept up by his Mae West, he drifted in of his own accord. The sun was strong on his face and he thought suddenly of the things he had thought about in the plane : the straw on the runways, his father eating the currants, the girl in the biscuit-coloured hat. He felt suddenly that they were the things for which he had struggled. They were his life. The waves took him gradually farther and farther up the shore, until his knees beat on the sand. He saw Carmichael and Johnson and Hargreaves waiting on the shore. At last new waves took him far up the shore until he lay still on the wet slope of sand and his arms were outstretched to the sky.

As he lay there the sea ran down over his body and receded away. It was warm and gentle on his hands and he was afraid of it no longer.

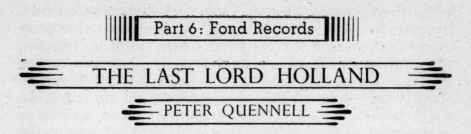

THE LAST LORD HOLLAND

PETER QUENNELL

One of the pleasantest of nineteenth century conversation pictures shows the interior of the long library at Holland House. Lord Holland, a benevolent pyramidal shape, is examining some bibliographical rarity that John Allen, the Hollands' literary adviser, factotum and familiar friend of many years' standing, has just presented ; William Doggett, the librarian, hovers nearby with a folio beneath his arm ; and Lady Holland, ringleted, shawled and ribboned, an osprey in her hat and a large fan protecting an elderly cheek against the rays of the afternoon sun, turns on the painter a bright, imperious, somewhat unfriendly glance. Here, in the persons of husband, wife and confidant, we have the three founders and supporters of one of the most remarkable creations of early nineteenth century social and intellectual life. Something of their exceptional character, it is true, Holland House gatherings owed to their position in time and to the fact that they represented a fusion of periods. Lady Holland, the fervent admirer—one might almost say, the patroness —of the Emperor Napoleon (whom she helped to comfort in his exile at St. Helena by regular shipments of preserved plums and other delicacies) lived on into the heart of the Victorian age ; and the same hostess who had opened her doors to Sheridan and, in a later generation, Byron, extended her friendship to Dickens, Thackeray and Macaulay.

Perhaps 'friendship' is hardly the word : for Lady Holland was an autocrat. As sometimes happens in marriage, the long and tender devotion that united the Hollands—beginning with a romantic elopement and terminating only with the conclusion of Lord Holland's life—seems to have been based on the complete incongruity of their personal dispositions. Lord Holland, 'a great grig and a great love,' was all patience, good humour and benevolent commonsense. His wife, egotistical, capricious and exacting, had a strain of downright malevolence in her distinctively feminine nature, inspired fear more often than love, and triumphed

P   217

by sheer impertinence when she could not command by intellect. Her tyranny was impartial, however—exercised now on her gouty enormous husband whom she forcibly deprived of his crutches, or with whom she refused to sit down to dinner till he had changed his waistcoat : now on casual acquaintances, without distinction of sex or age, whom she obliged to grovel for the fan or bag she was perpetually dropping : now on old friends whom, if a page or favourite footman had fallen ill, she would carry off to sit on the end of his bed, greatly to the joint confusion of invalid and visitor.

Yet, intolerable as her exactions often seemed, she was none the less inimitable. To Holland House and the standards it continued to support—even when Lord Holland had been dead for several years—there was no exact equivalent. It epitomised that curious phenomenon, the aristocratic liberalism of the late eighteenth and early nineteenth centuries, which Lord Holland had inherited from his more celebrated and yet more brilliant uncle, Charles James Fox. Its spirit was agnostic : the sympathies that inspired it were wide and generous. It combined deep learning with a profound appreciation of worldly pleasures ; and when Lord Holland remarked to a schoolboy who, asked to choose a dinner for some special occasion, selected roast duck and green peas followed by apricot tart, that if in all the important decisions of life he chose as wisely he would be a great and good man, he expressed in simple form the benign catholicity of his tastes and outlook. Talk at Holland House ranged easily over every conceivable subject, from ancient philosophy to contemporary politics, and from Chaucer and Homer to the novels of Jane Austen. Invariably well-informed, frequently erudite, it had at its best, among such talkers as Lord Holland, John Allen and William Lamb, none of that Victorian parade of learning for learning's sake which surprised and offended Sydney Smith in the dinner-table conversation of Macaulay.

Holland House, of course, was a stronghold of enlightened opposition. And it is perhaps not altogether to be regretted that, apart from one brief inconclusive expedition into office, the Whigs were to remain in dignified opposition till the formation of Lord Grey's government in 1830. For the moral foundations of Whig society were not entirely solid. Lady Holland, like Byron, managed to combine liberalism with a cult of the Napoleonic legend : the most prominent Whig magnates were extremely wealthy ; and, while Lord Durham—Creevey's 'King Jog'—

derived his vast income from northern coalmines, much of the Hollands' money came from Lady Holland's West-Indian plantations which ceased to yield a revenue when the Slave Trade was at length abolished.

YET, HOWEVER INCONGRUOUS the root, the flower was magnificent. It is interesting, then, to observe how under the influence of a new age, and in the lives of a new Victorian generation, aristocratic Whiggery began to lose its power as virtuosity replaced gusto, and dilettantism the vivid inquiring intelligence of an earlier and heartier epoch. The story is sad yet, so far as Holland House is concerned, redeemed from insignificance by the sensitiveness and acute, though limited, perceptions of one of the chief actors. Henry Edward Fox, fourth and last Lord Holland, was his parents' second surviving son. Their eldest son had been born out of wedlock, at a time when the runaway wife of Sir Godfrey Webster had not yet had an opportunity of legitimising the union she had contracted in Italy ; and it was Henry Edward, therefore, who expected to inherit the title. No doubt the odd position in which he found himself, as the involuntary rival of a brother to whom he was much attached, did something to exaggerate his natural melancholy. But—more important—Henry Fox had been born lame. This similarity in their inheritance had caused Byron to notice and befriend him at Holland House ; and, according to a pencil jotting by Hobhouse scribbled on the margin of Moore's biography, the poet had had occasion to speak reprovingly to Lady Holland because she scolded her son for being lame and awkward. Such humiliations in adolescence are not easily lived down. Fox seems to have admired his mother, but he did not love her. Quite apart from any acerbities he may have recollected, the effect upon a young and impressionable mind of contact with so determined and unscrupulous a personality was bound in the long run to be a trifle crushing ; and he was neither sufficiently self-confident nor sufficiently ruthless to resist her influence. The weaker nature resented the former, but could not shake off its spell. Towards the whole of life he acquired little by little a faintly querulous attitude.

To all this, add leisure, independence, the combined weight of an imposing tradition and an intensive education. Henry Fox was not built to carry so large a load : he had many virtues, but originality was not among them : his qualities were analytical

but not creative : and, to his own deep distress, he remained
always the talented looker-on, fidgeting in a ring-side seat, irritably
wideawake to the more ridiculous aspects of the scene before him.
Henry James might have considered him a congenial subject.
Against the background of the big Elizabethan country house
just outside London, and of London itself—still a city of eighteenth
century streets and squares, though cockney suburbs had begun to
pullulate upon its outskirts, and the farms and meadows that
encircled it were rapidly receding—that great master of the finer
shades would have depicted the complex development of his
hero's character. Lame children are often unusually precocious.
At the age of seventeen Henry Fox began to keep a journal ;
but, without reference to the date—he had been born in March
1802, and the first entry is dated December 16th, 1818—it would
be hard to determine the period of the writer's life at which it was
composed. The general tone is one of mild acrimony and middle-
aged detachment. Thanks to his lameness Fox was spared the
rigours of an English public school ; at Oxford he did not succeed ;
but at home, among his mother's and his father's friends, 'fashion-
ables,' 'Blues,' statesmen and professional diners-out, he soon
acquired the prevailing standards of Whig society. But they were
coloured, in Henry Fox's mind, by a vein of diffidence verging on
melancholy, and of scepticism tinged with personal embitterment.
Love—affection—admiration were all attractive. But how hard
for the entirely honest man not to perceive at once the disadvan-
tageous—the positively ridiculous—side of every human situation
and every emotional tie : to accept friendship without a second
thought, when first impulses so frequently proved disastrous :
to throw himself wholeheartedly into the arms of passion when,
in his friends' lives, he saw the grotesque consequences to which
passion led !

The *Journal*[1] is not in the ordinary sense an effort at heart-
searching. Yet through it always runs a nostalgic appreciation
of just those qualities—spontaneity, vitality, perhaps even generosity—in which the author understood that he was most deficient.
Oh, to be as other men (he may have sometimes sighed)—a
feather-headed dandy like the notorious Lord Petersham (who
'poor man ! . . . has nothing to do, and spends his morning in
snuff and teashops and his evenings at the theatre, and yet is

[1] THE JOURNAL OF THE HON. EDWARD FOX, edited by the Earl of
Ilchester, 1923

happy and contented') : a gambler and *viveur* like 'Punch'
Greville (who, had Henry Fox known it, was himself devoured by
a perpetual sense of inner insufficiency) : an exuberant talker like
Sydney Smith : or a famous poet and romantic amorist like Lord
Byron ! Not that Fox was either abstemious or puritanical. A
succession of young women—some married and adventurous,
some unmarried but perfectly prepared to accept the legitimate
advances of so eligible a suitor—engaged his interest during
London seasons or Italian holidays. He liked women, it is evident,
but he mistrusted love affairs. As soon as the footlights had begun
to go up, he was already foreseeing the gloom and oblivion of the
theatre when the stage had been deserted.

Consequently he often tormented his mistresses, and was
himself afterwards tormented by a consciousness of the harm he
felt he might have done. The penultimate paragraph of his
Journal (written in 1830, at the age of twenty-eight) dwells
despondently on the record of his emotional entanglements, more
or less serious, during the last twelve months :

> I look back upon life with much repentance. Not for the ambitious
> objects I have slighted, for had I attained them I should not be
> happier, and had I failed in the attempt, which is more likely, I
> should have been mortified and miserable. But I have cruelly and
> wantonly played with the feelings of others ; I have never believed
> anyone attached to me, and I have on that account, and on that
> account only, and not from the fickleness of which I am accused,
> determined not to be myself attached. My conduct towards Miss V.,
> Mlle P., and Ly. N. leave me much to regret—especially the last two
> instances. In the former there was much scheming and duplicity.

It is possible that the victims designated as V., P., and N.
(initials which stand for the names Villiers, Potocka and North-
ampton) were in less danger from the diarist's caprice than he
himself imagined—he would appear, in spite of his vein of petul-
ance, to have been on the whole kind-hearted and good-mannered
—and that they were puzzled by his evasions rather than deeply
wounded ; but the paragraph gives us a clue to his emotional
temperament. Fox was a cynic without the cynic's armour :
a child of the eighteenth century, he lived to witness the triumph
of the romantic movement and the evolution, moral and political,
of Victorian England. His senior in years, Byron, possessed by
comparison a distinctly Victorian side ; and it is odd that the
heroine of the poet's last serious love affair, the effusive and ultra-

romantic Teresa Guiccioli, should have become for a short time after Byron's death the mistress of the good-looking lame boy whom Childe Harold had befriended. Henry Fox accepted this curious conquest with moderate good grace. Not for him were the excitements of romantic self-surrender ! Surprised that Countess Guiccioli should have set her cap at him, he returned her ardours—but coolly and cautiously, and declined to be swept away.

THE EPISODE—one of the most entertaining in Henry Fox's fragmentary but extremely diverting narrative—occurred during a long visit to France and Italy between 1824 and 1826. Byron's friends had never shared his admiration for the young Italian married woman. Leigh Hunt had called her a 'buxom parlour boarder' ; Tom Moore had voted her at first sight 'not very pretty' ; and Fox, on being presented at a dinner party given by Lady Davy in 1824, pronounced her 'coarse, and far from being, to my taste, the least attractive. Her hair is nearly red, her figure squat, and her eyes have no expression but what with study she contrives to throw into them.' The introduction took place in Rome. A few days later, Henry Fox set out for Naples, whence he presently departed on a Grecian tour by way of Corfu, Cephalonia, Patras and Missolonghi. Back in Naples during the summer of 1825, he once again encountered the Countess Guiccioli— 'fresh from Rome (he noted), full of sentiment and absurdity.' He supposed she must be 'in search of an adventure' and wanted to 'fix herself upon some *handsome* and *illustrious* man. . . .' Having finished that entry, he laid his pen aside : to take it up again with a—for Henry Fox—slightly startled but characteristically dis-passionate observation : 'Strange as it may seem (he added) after having written the above paragraph, I find myself now, on the 9th of August, when taking up my pen to continue this diary, to have to record that though neither *handsome* nor *illustrious* I am, strange to say, become the object of T. G.'s affection.'

Possibly he was flattered : certainly he was not enthusiastic. Another young man of Henry Fox's age might have made haste to erase from his mind and journal the ungracious remarks he had first recorded there and, by simulating passion, come at length to feel it. The sad lucidity, however, with which he was blessed or cursed deprived Henry Fox of the chance of thus adding to his satisfaction ; and he remained conscious both of the artificiality of Teresa's feeling for him and of his own inability to play a truly romantic rôle. From 'moonlight sentimental walks' he had been not averse. 'I observed Teresa rather sought than shrunk from proffered civilities' ; and one Sunday evening on a balcony she had 'listened and consented. . . . Sentiment or caprice would not permit her to yield then . . . ' ; but she had appointed him the following night and received him, when the time came, with passionate abandon. 'I was not prepared for the extreme facility of the conquest which (such is the perverseness of one's nature) scarcely gave me pleasure.' She was 'too gross and too carnal' ; her manners were bad and her speech affected ; and he was much alarmed when she talked to him of five years' constancy !

Nevertheless (he recorded in his usual temperate vein), 'we had several agreeable evenings together, especially one night we went to Nisida and landed in my little favourite bay.' Music and moonlight may be potent drugs : more powerful, on some natures, is the effect of habit. Sufficiently honest with himself to admit that his behaviour had a somewhat shabby side—'. . . I felt rather ashamed of affecting sentiment I did not feel and of professing unalterable attachment'—he was also sincere enough to admit her qualities and to acknowledge that she 'occupied and to a degree amused' him. Her best point, he discovered, was her complete sincerity ; for—a very fine distinction—'though her sentiment is assumed, she believes it to be real.' It was true that she had no delicacy ; but then, she had 'no hypocrisy even of modesty. . . . She is a woman of very strong passions, and imagines she has very strong sentiments—but vast is the difference.'

As might have been expected, there were frequent scenes. Teresa proved 'jealous and exigeante and troublesome.' Poor Lord Byron ! Fox reflected : one was not surprised that he had exchanged life in Italy for death in Greece ; and, when Teresa 'after several quarrels and reconciliations' left Naples on October 15 and returned to Rome, he was almost relieved that a riding accident and a badly bruised ankle made it impossible for him to follow. Henceforward the relationship suffered a slow decline. During 1826 Henry Fox was recalled to England, where he had consented to take a seat in Parliament provided his parents would agree to his marriage with Theresa Villiers, a young woman to whom he had long been deeply if vaguely devoted ; but both plans fell through and he was soon on the wing again. His peregrinations eventually brought him back into Teresa's orbit. She awaited him, little changed and just as overpowering ; but habit prevailed and, having dined with her *tête-à-tête* on numerous occasions and driven masked to the Corso and 'pelted sugar plums'—for the Carnival was in full swing with balls and revelries —he decided that she was 'agreeable, and looked very well. . . . Her frankness and sincerity are unparalleled among all the women I have ever known, and her affectation . . . arises from trying in society to assume manners . . . to obtain which she has never had opportunities, or during her connection with Ld. B. the least desire . . . she is clever . . . I was surprized at her knowing so much of *Hamlet* by heart.'

The final scene—most appropriately—was staged in Naples, its setting the very balcony on which Teresa had 'listened and consented.' A 'very painful and extraordinary conversation' it turned out to be. 'Here . . . in 1825, our first amatory conversation took place, and to-night we each pretended to be taking an eternal farewell.' Teresa explained to Fox that the place he had left vacant had at length been filled (though at heart, she insinuated, 'she can love only me') and that his successor was an English dandy, Lord Fitzharris (the future Lord Malmesbury), 'an affected young man, very handsome, and extremely flattered by having obtained success with T. G.—a triumph he seems to suppose hitherto unheard of.' Teresa Guiccioli, however, was not the type of woman whose taste for farewell scenes is easily satisfied ; and a second parting occurred a few days later :

> I went in the morning (wrote Henry Fox on June 27) to take leave of T. G. We took a tender leave. I shall always feel excessive interest and regard for T. G., and I think she has shewn much generosity and nobleness of character on many occasions. Certainly her conduct to me has always been most admirable, considering my very unpardonable neglect of her ; nor can I the least blame her for taking a fresh lover when I had deserted her in the manner I had done.

Thus they separated—Teresa to pursue her predestined path, to be handed down from admirer to admirer, eventually from generation to generation, as a sort of amatory heirloom or precious sentimental and literary relic (enclosed in a reliquary that grew more ponderous as the years went by) till she ended her existence in a Parisian drawing-room, posing for her guests beneath Childe Harold's portrait and introduced by her second husband as '*Madame la marquise de Boissy, ma femme, ci-devant maîtresse de Lord Byron*' : Henry Fox to follow the desultory promptings of his heart and temperament. That his literary gifts were those of the amateur will be obvious from the passages I have already quoted. Beside the productions of Creevey or Greville, of Lady Granville or Lady Bessborough, his Journal is lacking in dash and descriptive brilliance—there are no set-pieces and few sustained attempts at rendering dialogue—yet for one reader at least it possesses its own peculiar charm. Henry Fox had that kind of bleak, slightly priggish honesty towards himself which is not always consistent with amiability towards one's fellows. He refused to record a sentiment he did not really feel ; he declined to remain the dupe of impulsive first impressions ; and repeatedly—sometimes, pettishly—he would revise the list of his acquaintances and admit that he had been hurt or disappointed by a friend's behaviour.

VERY OFTEN his disappointment seems to have been perfectly justified. Towards Alfred d'Orsay, for example, he had felt in the first instance a spontaneous and very strong attraction. Plainly he was a trifle dazzled by that magnificent youthful figure, in all the glory of health and strength and talent, all the splendour of watch-chains and whiskers and rings and waistcoats, primrose yellow gloves and exquisitely varnished boots. Lady Blessington, it is true, showy, pushing and insincere, with her damaged reputation and vulgar Irish brogue, he liked as little as he did her 'drivelling' husband. But 'le beau Alfred,' if equally suspect, was far more sympathetic :

> My friendship (wrote Fox) with Alfred is a warm one, but quite different from any I feel or ever have felt for anybody else. I admire some of his qualities and talents, and think he is by nature good-hearted and full of many estimable feelings and impulses ; but vanity, vanity with a good deal of false exaggerated pride, have so disfigured his character that they have turned his merits almost into defects. Besides, the fatal liaison with such a woman as L^y Blessington is calculated to do him a terrible deal of harm, living as he does the solitary life of an idol incensed by flattery. . . .

And with the indignation peculiar to cold and mistrustful men, who have for once obeyed the callings of the heart rather than the rules of the head, only to be reminded again that the heart is a deceptive counsellor, Henry Fox heard the squalid story of d'Orsay's projected marriage. Asked to act as witness at the ceremony that was to unite Lady Blessington's lover to her helpless fifteen-year-old stepdaughter, Lady Harriet Gardiner, Fox flatly refused and set forth his reasons. D'Orsay's reply was ingenuous but not disarming—'he only makes bad worse by professing his connection with Lady B., his indifference to the hapless bride, and the many advantages of fortune, &c., &c., he hopes to acquire'— and their association presently degenerated into overt hatred.

Such shocks, though disagreeable, dealt merely a glancing blow. More important in Henry Fox's life, more decisive in its effect upon his character, was his relationship with his mother and father and sister, and with the whole Holland House tradition of which he was expected to form a part. During his father's lifetime the position had been bad enough. Where the world saw a not unpleasing balance of opposites—Lord Holland's invariable amiability in contrast to Lady Holland's termagant oddities—Henry Fox saw the tragic subjection of a weak, good-natured father to a mother whose dominant trait was her devouring egotism. He deplored and protested against the nursery seclusion in which Lady Holland—capricious matriarch—was determined that his sister should be brought up ; and, when Mary Fox had married, and Lord Holland had succumbed to his infirmities in 1840, 'My Lady' at every turn was still an obstructive influence. His father had left her Holland House during her lifetime, and all the contents, including a valuable library, to dispose of as she pleased. Five years longer she continued to harass her children and spoil her dependants, issue commands, give dinner parties and consult innumerable specialists on the subject of her health. Yet, when death came, she received it with perfect *sang-froid*, with complete resignation but not the smallest touch of religious feeling. An old acquaintance, 'Punch' Greville, composed her epitaph :

> Though she was a woman (he observed) for whom nobody felt any affection, and whose death therefore will have excited no grief, she will be regretted by a great many people, some from kindly, more from selfish motives ; and all who had been accustomed to live at Holland House, and continued to be its habitués, will lament over the fall of the curtain on that long drama, and the final extinction of the flickering remnant of social light which illuminated and adorned England, and even Europe, for half a century. The world never has seen and never will again see anything like Holland House. . . .

Henry Fox (now fourth Lord Holland) survived the dowager Lady Holland till 1859 ; but for him too, in some mysterious fashion, the curtain seemed to have gone down. In 1833 he had married : various diplomatic appointments had come his way :

after the matriarch's death he spent much of his time in Kensington and more money than he could afford in restorations and 'improvements' ; but during those latter years it is difficult to feel in him a very lively interest. Fiercely as he had sometimes fretted against it, he belonged to his parents' world. The young man who had known Byron and Alfred d'Orsay, who had obstinately refused to catch the eye of 'that little viper,' the incorrigible Lady Caroline Lamb, and who remembered her mother, one of the most brilliant letter-writers of her generation, the always agitated and effusive Lady Bessborough, paying a distracted visit to Holland House, 'of course in a great hurry' and of course leaving 'her bag and pocket-handkerchief and smelling-bottle in three separate rooms,' could have little in common with the social background of the mid-Victorian age. Unlike many of his contemporaries, he had no gift of compromise or assimilation ; and the main current of the period had passed him by. While Henry Fox continued to potter about his gardens, build a new staircase or commission his friend Watts to paint him family portraits, London in a dark flood encircled his ancestral domains and spread beyond in wave on wave of streets and terraces. Over the green crests of the plantations surrounding Holland Park had begun to peer the gaunt chimneypots of the suburban skyline.

THE FLEET OF FOOT

BERNARD DARWIN

'Billy Jackson (the American Deer), J. Davies (the Lame Chicken) and Tom Maxfield (the North Star), ran a mile match upon the Slough Road, over what is still known as Maxfield's Mile, amidst an enormous concourse and immense enthusiasm.' I have been murmuring that sentence to myself just as I did some 54 years ago, when it first kindled in my youthful breast a passion for running. If it has always been a romantic rather than a practical one, it has been, I fancy, all the more ardent for that. In the previous year I had seen the University Sports at Fenners. I had even run upon that famous track myself in two races for schoolboys of tender years and won a cup and a silver-mounted marmalade jar of hideous aspect. But it was the North Star that did it. Can there be anyone so lost to all the better feelings of humanity that he does not feel a shiver of emotion down the spine at such noble names as these ?

To me they have always been irresistible and I have just been spending a happy afternoon in their company. It might not suit everybody, but to me it represents the very quintessence of romance. Outside is a hushed world of snowdrifts. All day long no car has passed along the road, save only that of one heroic, life-saving baker. There is no sound to break the stillness but the plump, plump of snow which is being shovelled off the roof and the roaring and crackling of a fire. My chair is drawn up close to it and on my lap is the dear old *Badminton* volume on Athletics, containing that immortal sentence. Not far off, where I can feast my eyes upon them when so disposed, are two prints : one shows Captain Barclay in the course of achieving his thousand miles in a thousand hours at Newmarket. In the other the famous Deerfoot is racing home to victory against an adversary who may be Jack White or Lang or haply Siah Albison.

These two works of art differ as widely in merit as do their two heroes in appearance. Captain Barclay stands alone in the light of a lamp which guides him on his midnight path, with a dim landscape in the background. It is a charming print, delicate in colour ; and Barclay in his tall hat, with a yellow handkerchief knotted round his neck, looks what he was, a sporting gentleman of ancient lineage and unimpeachable respectability. Yet I almost think that I am fonder of the other print, which is rather coarse and garish in colour and not in the least well drawn. Yet who shall stand against this resistless Deerfoot ? He is attired in his full fig as a Canadian Indian (his real name was L. Bennett, but we can forget that). Bound to his brow by a gold band is a grey owl's feather. Moccasins are on his feet. His only other garment is a short petticoat, if I may so term it, of red, blue and yellow feathers. Either his adversary, clad apparently in button boots, is very small or Deerfoot has been drawn something larger than life-size to emphasise his greatness. He towers over all the spectators, an aggregation of rather flash and squalid-looking persons, some of them with betting book in hand. The scene is apparently a suburban road, with trees and houses, and I like to fancy that it is on Clapham Common. There is no justification whatever for this, but my father was at a school at Clapham at about this period, and used to tell me about Deerfoot who had stirred the schoolboy imagination.

How could he fail to do so with such a name as that? The conferring of these lovely names seems to be a lost art. Perhaps we ourselves have changed. When I was a small boy living at Cambridge there was a famous University eight that rowed unchanged, save for a new cox, two years running. Those two immortals, Muttlebury and Gardner, rowed in it. It was called 'The Lightning Crew,' and I went timidly into Messrs. Stearns' shop and bought a photograph of it which I still possess. Then that name seemed to me supremely exciting and beautiful; to-day I am afraid I should only regard it as the poor and vulgar invention of some sporting journalist. And yet—and yet there was the North Star and there was the Greenwich Cowboy. And what of Skewball, the famous Lancashire Shepherd who was supposed to have run 140 yards in 12 seconds at Hackney? Is not that a name to thrill? And then perhaps best of all there was the Suffolk Stag.

'When George Frost (the Suffolk Stag) won the Championship belt at the Old Copenhagen Grounds by a ten mile race, lithographs of the contest were published and sold by the thousand.' That was another sentence which I loved and rolled on my tongue, and yet it drove me frantic; the lithograph had once been sold to thousands and now there was 'never ah! never a one for me.' That grievance has since been put right, for one happy day my wife saw one in the Fulham Road and, without realising the full extent of her benefaction, brought it home in triumph for me. I am at the moment an exile and so I am parted from the Stag as I am from Tom Cribb and Molineaux, Peter Crawley the Young Rump Steak, George Osbaldeston, Fuller Pilch and others of my friends. However, I can see him clearly in the mind's eye. Mr Frost is a young gentleman of mild, almost curatical, aspect, stripped to the waist and clad only in short white drawers, skimming over the ground on a pair of long thin pointed feet. There is no trace of J. Levett, whom according to the inscription he defeated on that glorious day, but below, a miracle of blue and silver, is THE BELT.

I have since found out a little more about Mr Frost which shows that he was not alas! quite so innocent and virtuous a person as he looked; but the story is an interesting one as casting a light on the morals of pedestrianism of that day—1853. It is to be found in *Years of My Life*, by the late Sir John Astley, famous as 'The Mate,' who was in his youth a noted runner in money matches. It is rather a long story but I hope worth the re-telling. Captain Astley of the Scots Guards, as he then was, was stationed at Windsor, and the landlord of the inn Surly Hall, well known to generations of Eton boys, was in 1853 a retired runner. Captain Astley used the inn as a training stable for pedestrians, among whom was 'a man named Frost.' How lamentably practical and unromantic was Sir John to refer to him under this prosaic description ! Indeed, he was impervious to such beauties and spoke with contempt of the Bristol Mouse who had beaten the Newport Stag. Some time before this ten mile race Astley heard that Levett had, like a horse, 'been coughing' and expected some manœuvre on the part of his backer Dismore, 'an unscrupulous old party.' So he kept a sharp watch on his man and constantly visited Surly. One day he had punted up there from Windsor, when who should drive up in a trap but Levett with his backer, Dan Dismore. Astley locked Frost safely in his bedroom, pocketed the key and then hailed them from the window. They said they had only come to see Mr Frost. The Captain replied that here he was and they could say anything they wanted to him through the window. Mr Dismore deprecated such suspicious conduct and said in a wounded manner that in that case they would go away. Astley said he would go away too, started off in his punt and then hid behind an eyot. Sure enough back came the trap and back came Astley, who after a few more compliments saw them safely off at the station.

So far the plot had been foiled, but on the day of the race it thickened. The betting was 5 to 4 on Levett which made Captain Astley suspect something amiss. However, Frost went off with the lead according to his instructions and won with ease. As soon as the race was over Astley was warned that both he and his man had better be off, for there was trouble brewing. He hastened to his waiting cab and found the Stag with nothing on but his running kit and a rug. 'I put the double on 'em,' he said, and implored with obvious terror an instant departure. Off they went, and this was the story Frost told him in the cab. A man came to him in his dressing room with a pot of porter and said, 'If you drink this I'll give you a fifty-pound note.' 'No,' answered the astute Stag, 'but bring me a pint bottle corked with the wire on and I'll drink it ; stake your fifty pound.' The bottle was brought and drunk, and Frost tucked the banknote into his belt. As soon as his tempter had departed, he went on, 'I put my finger down my throat and got rid of the porter,' and that was why the other side was so angry. Captain Astley was angry too, although

Mr Frost pathetically urged, 'I behaved all right to you, Captain.' So by his own standards perhaps he had, but he never got another backer. Poor Stag ! I feel rather sorry for him.

I DON'T THINK I am a noticeably dishonest player of games, unless indeed in my younger days at Musical Chairs, when a little licence was generally allowed : but I like that story. I cannot deny that for me it adds a certain relish to the running of old days. It is the same when I read of the Derby of 1844, with two separate and individual conspiracies, one over Ratan and the other over Running Rein ; or of Mr Crommelin, in green spectacles and a large false moustache, going to meet Young John Day at a mysterious place of assignation, just to have a little friendly talk about the Melody Colt. I like the mysterious 'party in the know' stationed to 'give the office.' I like the train which started from London Bridge in the middle of the night for the Sayers and Heenan fight with the tickets marked simply 'There and Back.' It was doubtless a shoddy business of squalid ruffians, but distance seems to lend some strange enchantment to my view of them. And even among the amateurs there was a rather different standard of morals from that of to-day, and gentlemen of unquestioned honour did what we should now deem very singular things. An amateur, by the way, only meant a gentleman ; there were no nice questions of amateurism as we know them ; no nonsense, as it would then have been held, about not running for money or against a professional. Sir John himself, as a young man, habitually took about with him, in the guise of a servant, one Patterson, known as the Flying Tailor, and when they were practising together they took care to win alternately, lest there should be any shrewd person hiding behind a bush to see what he could see. When Astley went to stay anywhere he would send a message into the nearest town and challenge the best man there to run him for five pounds. From Norwich came the Norwich Pet to win the money, and after Astley had beaten him by a discreet distance, he taunted the Pet with his defeat and said, 'Why, my servant shall beat you.' Out came the Flying Tailor at the word and another five pounds changed hands. The poor Pet departed so crestfallen that he had to be consoled with 'a piece of gold.'

It all sounds to us to-day what Mr Michael Finsbury would have called 'pertaining to the finny tribe.' Everything was a match and that had no doubt something to do with it. There were no meetings with entry forms and handicaps and scrutinies of past performances and all the paraphernalia of modern athletics. There was a challenge and a stake and a match and, whatever the sport, the devil took the hindermost. A sound maxim for anyone embarking on a match would have been 'Caveat Emptor,' for there was always a good chance of buying a pig in a poke, and if you did there was no help for it. 'Play or Pay' was the one inexorable principle, and to chafe and fret your nervous adversary by being 'a wee bit tricky at the start' was all in the game. It was a fine simple principle and yet it was always leading to quarrels. Sometimes, as in one of Captain Astley's matches, there was at the end only 'a slight wrangle,' before the loser recognised that he had been slightly 'done' but had got to pay. At other times there was 'a tremendous wrangle' ; both sides claimed the stake and neither side would part with it. There was one such squabble as to which Sir John admitted that 'he had never been *quite* satisfied with his conduct on that occasion.' I am bound to say that he would have been rather easily satisfied if he had.

Nevertheless, he is a very engaging as well as a very ingenious old gentleman, and I cannot leave him without gratefully record-ing that in his pages I have discovered two of my dearest friends in their old age. When the American Deer was 72, he had fallen on bad days, and Sir John decided to give him a benefit. So he organised a ten mile race for men over fifty—rather a stern test, one would suppose, even though there was a start of fifty yards for every year over fifty. Thirty-three old fellows turned out, and the Deer himself ran, and ran well, until one of his ankles gave out. The race was won by Choppy Warburton (another old acquaintance of my *Badminton*), and then there was the typical 'wrangle.' Choppy had produced a printed birth certificate showing that he was over fifty, but a subsequent search at Somer-set House proved that he had made an unfortunate mistake. One can only hope the poor old Deer made something substantial out of the gate. In another part of the book there is a mention, all too cold and offhand for my hero-worshipping taste, of one of Sir John's opponents having gone to train at Slough 'under the care of a noted old ten-mile runner yclept the North Star.' Let me add that Slough still celebrates him, perhaps unconsciously. I shall never forget the thrill with which on first going to Eton I saw, on a Sunday walk, a public house bearing as its sign 'The North Star.' I hope and believe that it is there still.

ONE OF THE attractive things about many of these old matches was their comparatively casual nature. They were run, as it might be said, anywhere ; on the high road, such as Maxfield's Mile or the road into Newmarket on which Lang once ran a famous mile against time ; on the Long Walk at Windsor where the whole town turned out to see Captain Astley beat a trooper of the Life Guards ; on cricket grounds and race courses. There were very few tracks such as that on the Copenhagen ground, where Frost won his belt, generally known as 'the old Cope.' I pause for a moment to inquire whether it was there too that Hazlitt watched Cavanagh, the fives player. 'He used frequently to play matches at Copenhagen House for wagers and dinners. The wall against which they play is the same that supports the kitchen-chimney, and when the wall resounded louder than usual, the cooks exclaimed, "Those are the Irishman's balls," and the joints trembled on the spit !" ' However, this is pure meandering for the pleasure of transcribing a noble passage. Cricket grounds were favourite arenas, presumably because they were reasonably level and because many matches were the results of impromptu challenges from the best runner of the one eleven to any man on the other side. Many such races were run at Lord's, some of them by the great Lord Frederick Beauclerk, a mighty cricketer in his youth and in his old age the autocrat of the M.C.C. As that reverend nobleman—people are apt to forget that he was a Doctor of Divinity—used to boast that his cricket was worth £700 a year to him, he may be assumed to have made his matches with judgment. One he certainly did ; a hundred-yard race against the Hon. Mr Brand, who became 'quite winded before he had run fifty paces.' Lord Frederick was a little too young to have run against another celebrated cricketer of early days, Noah Mann, one of the champions of the Hambledon Club, who once hit a ball for ten on Windmill Down. 'He was all muscle,' said John Nyren, 'with no incumbrance whatever of flesh ; remarkably broad in the chest, with large hips and spider legs ; he had not an ounce of flesh about him but where it ought to be.' He was famed in all the country round for his swiftness, and whenever there was a cricket match the Hambledon men would try to get up a race for Noah against some noted runner. 'If,' he used to say, 'when we are half way you see me alongside of my man, you may always bet your money upon me, for I am sure to win,' and Nyren at least never saw him beaten. Noah

Q

was born seventeen years before Lord Frederick ; so in life the years kept them asunder, but if there is foot racing on the asphodel and the nobleman will so far condescend, I will back the gipsy.

These comparatively impromptu and post-prandial matches were naturally over short distances. A 100 or 150 yards was the favourite length, and we hear little of that perhaps most dramatic of all races, the quarter. The more solemn matches which drew the big crowds and the big bets were usually over long distances. They were apparently first made popular by Foster Powell, a lawyer's clerk, who when he was 59 went from London to York and back in 5 days 15¼ hours. From his time at the end of the eighteenth century to that of Deerfoot there was a more or less unbroken line of these long distance runners. The greatest, not in point of achievement perhaps judged by modern standards but in point of contemporary fame, was Captain Barclay Allardyce of Ury, in Aberdeenshire, who always ran under the name of Barclay. It was at Ury that he trained Tom Cribb for his match with the negro Molineaux and made him, in Dick Christian's words, 'fine as a star, just like snow aside a black man.' Poor Tom, who was at first fat and out of condition, ran terrible races after the Captain up the Scottish hills. The Captain flitted in front, like some malignant sprite, with a pocketful of pebbles with which ever and anon he bombarded his victim's shins, Tom pursuing vainly and apoplectically in hope of revenge.

Barclay's best known feat was the compassing of a thousand miles in a thousand hours before mentioned, after which he slept for a day and a night, being woken up every five hours on some mysterious scientific principle, and then set off on the ill-fated expedition to Walcheren. In that he was unlike many of his contemporaries, who went placidly on with their matches while the tents of Napoleon's camp at Boulogne could be seen on a clear day. He was a hard man, as hard on himself as he was on Tom Cribb, and of the type to which George Osbaldeston belonged, that had only to be dared to do something in order instantly to set about it. Having won a bet by driving the mail from London to Aberdeen, Barclay offered instantly to drive it back again, but the other party to the bet thought he looked too fresh and would have no more. One little instance of this amiable weakness I know not from books but from the talk of my kinsman, the late Sir Francis Galton. As a young man he met Captain Barclay, then an old one, at dinner. The conversation turned on some of the Captain's achievements and in particular on that of being able to lift a full grown man from the floor standing on his right hand while he steadied him with his left. The old gentleman promptly undertook to do it again after dinner and did, but he strained himself rather badly in the process. Still, he had said he could do it and he had done it, and that was all that mattered. He must have been an ill man to bet with.

I must leave these ancient heroes with their matches and their wagers and there go-as-you-please morality ; though I will not leave my beloved *Badminton* for a while, but turn to some later pages. Now we come to the days of Amateur Athletics in capital letters, with sports and tracks and amateur definitions. In these fascinating pages of Sir Montague Shearman are many illustrious names, down to those whom I myself saw and some even whom I knew well. When I read that book in youth I went on the well known principle *Omne ignotum pro magnifico*. The runners who held for me the highest romance were not necessarily the greatest, but those over whom hung some glamour of mystery, who appeared suddenly and then disappeared and nobody knew how tremendous they really were. Truly alluring, for instance, is the story of the Russian Junker, squat, square, clumsy and flat-footed who appears out of the blue for one brilliant season and then

> The meteor droops
> And in a flash expires.

It was only because he was chaffed about this clumsiness of his that he ever put on a shoe. Irritated by some facetious friends in the City, he declared he was a good runner. Since this sally only aroused the louder laughter, he offered to run his chief tormentor for a bottle of champagne, and beat him by untold yards. He thereupon joined the London Athletic Club, won the Hundred Yards Championship of 1878, and then apparently vanished. There is no more story, and we are left hungry.

It is a good story as far as it goes, but I like still better that of a great and mysterious miler, W. H. Seary, of much the same date. He was an Oxford scout, and trained in traversing Peck and Tom Quads on his lawful occasions. He won races against the best northern runners, and there is a murky romance and a terror about the north which alone are worth the money to the timid southerner. There was a great miler of those days, Walter Slade of the London Stock Exchange, who monopolised the

Championship from 1873 to 1877. Yorkshire and Lancashire
would have put their money on Seary against him, but in those
times the old tradition of the 'gentleman-amateur,' now only
preserved at Henley, still survived in athletic circles, and Seary's
entry for the Championship was refused. And so we shall never
know what he might have done. 'A superb runner with a long
stride and light of foot,' says Sir Montague Shearman, and that
was yet another of my favourite sentences. When I was thirteen
I used to think that Seary would have beaten Slade if he had been
allowed to try, and I am not going to give up my belief at this
time of day.

At this point the reader, if indeed he has got so far, may say
to me : 'Vell, now, you've been prophecyin' avay wery fine, like
a red-faced Nixon,' and go on to complain that I have talked
much of romance and excitement without giving any reasons for
the faith that is in me. It is not easy to explain the fascination of
foot-racing, but I think a good many people do not appreciate it
because they have never given themselves the chance. Sports
have, it cannot be denied, intervals of tedium. This may be
partly owing to preliminary practising and prancing and the
digging of starting holes with little trowels, though to the true
enthusiast this only heightens the delicious suspense. More to
blame are the hurling of heavy weights and the long time spent
over the jumps. Of the polejumpers indeed it may be said
(adapting a familiar quotation) that they

> Would tire the sun with jumping
> And send him down the sky.

Before the Hundred they are there, and when the Three Miles is
finishing they are there also. These things *are* a little dull, even
very dull : but they are a thousand times compensated for by the
racing, whether it be 'the surge and thunder' of the Hundred, the
agony of the Quarter, or the cumulative thrill of the Three Miles,
with its burst of clapping, rising steadily to a storm in the last lap.
There seems to me no pastime in which the onlooker shares with
a more painful pleasure the feelings of the competitor. This
is certainly so at the start when in imagination he hangs on the
mark in unutterable tension and prays for the pistol to be swift
and merciful. I once had a seat at the great Rugby football
match between Wales and New Zealand, behind a man who for
the last few minutes sat with his head in his hands groaning,

'Why doesn't that bloody whistle go ?' Such are the spectator's feelings at the start of a crucial hundred or quarter, waiting for the flash with the men breaking away and being called back, as it seems to all eternity. And then what a moment is that when after the thrust and parry, spurt and counter-spurt our man comes away, beyond all question, in the straight ! We say with a sigh of relief, 'He's got him,' and in another second or two the victor has flung himself into welcoming arms.

Moreover, running is, quite apart from its agony and its jubilation, a beautiful sight in itself, whether it be—to mention two illustrious Oxford runners—the light pattering of a Lovelock or the majestic stride, 'the pride and ample pinion' of a Cornwallis. For beauty of movement, even if it be a little meretricious and artificial, there is perhaps nothing better than a hurdle race, with its symmetry of rising and falling. I shall always remember with joy a great Canadian hurdler whom I once saw, Earl Thompson, the more impressive because a bigger man than hurdlers usually are. His chin seemed to go down almost to meet his knee as he skimmed each hurdle with the most perfect precision of which the human machine is capable. Still, I prefer my racing pure and simple without hurdles and, if I have got to choose, whether for sheer excitement or the sheer splendour of men running themselves to their last gasp, then give me a quarter.

Most of my own watching of foot races has been at the University Sports, and for a good many years I used to report them for *The Times*, until I was rightly superseded on account of the scandalously overt partisanship of my descriptions. I felt no bitterness whatever on that account, and have enjoyed the Sports even more as a free man who could whoop and bellow to his heart's content, without having to remember too accurately or coin phrases as he went along. In all those years it is, I think, the quarters that stand out most clearly in memory. First Monypenny, whom I saw as a schoolboy in my first Sports in 1892 : then Jordan with his red head and Fitzherbert with that tremendous lurching roll that seemed to fill the whole track ; Meyrick Hollins and Davison ; Gordon Davies beating Rudd in 1914, and so at long last sealing the doom of Oxford and their Rhodes Scholars ; Rudd and Butler dead-heating ; Macmillan and Black ; A. G. K. Browne and Pennington. These are a few random memories of great quarters and quarter-milers, and stay—there is one more, peculiarly vivid. There was one year in which H. M. Abrahams, besides his hardy annuals of the Hundred and the Long Jump, also undertook the Quarter, which was something beyond his distance. Oxford had Stevenson, a very fine American quarter-miler, who never did himself justice in our bleak spring weather. Abrahams went off at a tremendous pace—he always reminded me of some great bird—and when he turned into the straight held a long lead, but now his hard time was coming. Could he last that unaccustomed distance? Stevenson was coming up and up ; Abrahams coming back and back to him. Would the tape never come ? Pluck, resolution, and fitness brought Abrahams home, and that in a very fine time. In point of mere yards he almost won comfortably, but it had been, I am sure, 'a damned close-run thing,' and among all his victories I have always felt that there is none of which he ought to feel prouder than that one.

It is hard to say whether the Quarter is better or worse as a spectacle, now that it is run in 'lanes,' as is the Hundred. There is to-day no need for that frantic rush, with perhaps a little jostling, to get first to the first corner, no running wide in order to pass the man in front. I remember talking to that delightful person, the late Mr R. H. Macaulay, a famous Cambridge quarter-miler in his day, and he was very decided on the point that the older runners had to cover a great many extra yards as compared with the modern ones. I hope by the way that it is true—I never asked him—that he had laid down his pipe just before starting, won his race and found it still alight when he returned in triumph. When the race was run not in lanes the spectator could, of course, see exactly who was leading at any point. The present system, which is obviously the more fair, necessitates the runners starting so to speak *en échelon*, in order that each may have the same distance to cover, and consequently the race has at first sight the appearance of a handicap. It is difficult, except no doubt to the highly experienced eye, to tell in the early stages of the race, who is ahead. This is at once exasperating and exciting, and it is only when the men turn into the straight for home that one can see exactly what has happened and what is probably going to happen. And now there comes back to me yet one more quarter, in the old manner at Queen's Club, which I must give myself the pleasure of describing. Perhaps it appeals to my liking of the tortuous ways of the Suffolk Stag, because the enemy were, I hasten to say in a strictly honourable manner, 'led up the garden path.' It was in

1899, in a match between Oxford and Cambridge and two American Universities. Our pair were Meyrick Hollins of Oxford, who had been at my tutor's at Eton, and Davison of Cambridge. In the University Sports in the spring Hollins had won, but this was summer ; he had been playing cricket and had had little time to get thoroughly fit. So he and Davison had by private arrangement changed places, and he played the part of second string. This the Americans naturally did not know ; they knew that he was No. 1, and when he set out at a terrific pace they went after him for all they were worth, with Davison lying last well behind. After 300 yards or so Hollins in effect gave up, the two Americans had exhausted themselves in pursuing him, and Davison, coming up with his long stride, sailed past them to win comfortably in, I think, $49\frac{2}{5}$ seconds. It was a very pretty little piece of tactics, admirably executed.

For pure venomous happiness I remember no race to equal the half mile in 1914 in which Atkinson of Cambridge beat Taber, an American at Oxford, a beautiful runner and an Olympic miler of great fame. Atkinson was a converted three-miler, as I remember, and anything but an elegant runner ; so when, labouring and rolling, he dashed ahead of Taber up the back stretch it was thought merely a gallant and expiring effort. And then—oh ! miraculous circumstance which the reader cannot conceivably have expected—he rolled further and further ahead and won easily. However, I must not let my Cambridge feelings get altogether too strong for me. Let me turn to an Oxford victory, that of Lovelock against the American Bonthron. This was almost the first of those Miles picturesquely called 'The Mile of the Century' ; Bonthron had done wonderful times at home, and the expectant hush before the race started was something that I do not remember before any other. Indeed, it was the best part of it for, save that the right man won, the race was disappointing. Bonthron ran easily and gracefully but a thought mechanically and without much dash ; Lovelock pit-a-patted along behind him full of life, and when he chose to make his effort it was all over. There was much cheering, of course, and there is no sound that comes nearer to tears than that gradually swelling roar as the winner draws closer and closer to the tape ; but, as far as the race was concerned, there was nothing to compare with that breathless wait before the start. That race was only relatively disappointing, and, indeed, if our own man wins too much sympathy need never be wasted on us. A real and bitter disappointment was at a Championship meeting when I proposed to myself to see the incomparable Nurmi win the mile. For some reason that I do not know he elected not to run in the mile but in the steeplechase instead. He won with utter ease, stop watch in hand, and gave the impression of an untiring and remorseless steam engine, but nothing could atone for the mile, and I never saw him again.

One mile that I remember with pure joy was the School Mile at Eton, in the Easter half of 1893. It was run in those days on the Dorney Road, and I am glad to think that I have seen a mile race on a road, such as the North Star had won, and not so very far away. It is, in fact, a very dull race to watch as compared with one on a track, since, unless the spectator accompanies it on a bicycle, he sees little but the end. We assembled near the finish and strained our eyes up the road for the first sight of the leader. When we saw him it was the right leader, at least for all Collegers, for it was Jack Fremantle, afterwards a triple victor in the Three Miles for Oxford, then barely seventeen, a small and obscure Colleger without a single 'colour' with which to bless himself. I can see him now, a little figure in grey shorts, romping in yards and yards ahead of the Oppidan hordes : and the time seemed almost too good to be true, for it was 4 minutes 32¼ seconds. To be sure he had a good fresh wind blowing behind him down the Dorney road, and a time in those circumstances would never be accepted as a 'record' ; but he was a mighty runner and my College patriotism is still so strong that I rejoice that no Cambridge man ever succeeded in beating him.

And now let me end as I began with yet one more sentence that I know almost by heart from my *Badminton*. It belongs to a much earlier time than the others, for it comes from Mr Pepys under the date of July 30, 1663. 'The towne talk this day is of nothing but the great foot-race run this day on Banstead Downes, between Lee, the Duke of Richmond's footman, and a tyler, a famous runner. And Lee hath beat him ; though the King and the Duke of York, and all men almost, did bet three to four to one upon the tyler's head.' The odds were certainly long, and perhaps some black-vizarded ruffian brought the tyler a pot of porter before the race. The Suffolk Stag was not, I imagine, the first of his kind, and there was probably much wisdom in the advice of an old book-maker, 'Never back anything as can talk.'

ALL THE YEAR ROUND

Wood engravings by AGNES MILLER PARKER

Commentary by H. E. BATES

Staring at the fire and beyond the fire into the space of centuries, does the cat see the constancy of herself through thousands of years? She is the only wild animal that is tame, the only tame one that is also wild. She is the tiger in the grass : she waits for the sparrow, the mouse, the rabbit, the leveret, the rat, the fish. Is it time to put out the light and go to bed ? You slap in the bolt of the door and she is happy in the darkness and the rain.

R

The spaniel bounds over the snow, stirring wild duck from the doddle-willows : silly, affectionate, noble, dependent thing. Leaping over the frozen reeds it pretends, unlike the cat by the fire, to be a creature of the wild. All the time there is something missing : man, without whom it cannot exist ; the stick for which it is running ; the basket in the kitchen. What do we see in dogs ?—the ridiculous little dachshund, the naked poodle, the popinjay Peke, the meat-eating mastiff, the archduke Borzoi ? Do we keep them because they give us a sense of mastery ? It is always the dog and his master, never the cat and his master. Down dog, up Fido, still now, fetch it ! Do we like the feeling of command ? The dog fetches our slippers and sets them by the fire, runs for the stick thrown over the snow, looks up at us with dark, irresistible, fathomless eyes. Isn't it strange that we never turn him out into the darkness and the rain ?

There are two seasons when the hare looks at its best : in March, on the ploughlands, when you may see six or seven or even a dozen racing in the mad circles of courtship ; and again in high summer, when the corn is ripe and the young leverets are big enough to run. The hare's eyes are set back in the head, so that, when running, it can literally look backwards. But by looking backwards for danger it often runs forward into danger. Hares may be caught when skulking in the ripe corn. You find them crouching immobilised, almost as if hypnotised, in the sun-warmed earth between the sheaves, and you spread your hands forward as if you are saying 'Sssh !' to someone, and the eyes of the hare are livid white as he watches you and waits, and you fall at last on your face and feel the bounding body of the hare beating against your heart—if he isn't already over the hill into another county.

April is often cold on the Downs ; the lambs are late with us. The primroses come with Christmas, even under snow. First there are very few. Then by February they begin to shine under the trees, still sparse, but stronger, until in March and April they are luxuriant and floppy and pink-stemmed on the steep banks where the lambs lie down and sleep in the sun. When the lambs are surprised and woken they make for the ewes with finicky gallop, and bunt with great vigour at the teats while the ewes stare with wooden animosity. Then the lambs calm down and look at you, heads aside, perky, and then suddenly dash off again, bouncing in indiarubber leaps off the grass. By the time June has come they are like thick wooden toys in the paddocks among the moon-daisies, and it is not easy to remember them as they were, asleep among the primroses or bouncing on the grass.

244

The cows come down into the long meadow from the farm above the church between four and five on summer afternoons. They amble straight for the farther end, where the stream is deeper, and they come to drink there in a pool under an alder-tree, where the roach are good in the swim between the reeds. On very hot days they cool their hocks in the water, and there is a warm heavy cow-smell in the shade. Fish jump in the deep pools where there is no sunlight and a kingfisher sweeps up the narrow reaches, blue in the air, copper in the water. When they have finished drinking the cows squelch backwards along the stream, and the water curdles and clears again, and they amble away across the meadow to find shade under the oaks on the far side. When they have settled in the shade there is no movement except the flight of the kingfisher and the trembling of the dragon flies in the reeds.

In England the forests have almost gone, the wild deer with them ;
but when I drive across great parks, such as Cowdray in Sussex,
and see deer placidly feeding under the oak trees, I think of Queen
Anne who, 'as she was journeying on the Portsmouth road, did
not think the Forest of Wolmer beneath her royal regard. For
she came out,' says Gilbert White, 'of the great road at Liphook,
which is just by, and reposed on a bank smoothed for that purpose,
lying about half a mile to the east of Wolmer-pond, and still
called Queen's bank, saw with great complacency and satisfaction
the whole herd of red deer brought by the keepers along the
vale before her, consisting then of about five hundred head.'
Pleasant to think of that specially smoothed bank, of the humanity
of monarchs, of the beauty of deer. Both deer and monarchs
have been becoming extinct in Europe for a long time. Pleasant
to think how, in England, in times of dislocation, both survive.

Red fox, red deer, red squirrel : the tawny brightness gets rarer and rarer. Grey squirrels are to red squirrels what sparrows are to bull-finches. But watch them through field glasses and note how, sitting up, crouching, bouncing over the grass, they look like other animals : crouching, flat-bellied against the earth, like grey rats ; crouching, head on fore-paws, like young lionesses ; sitting upright, hind legs pouching, like kangaroos. Their shyness will not let you get near enough to see all this with the naked eye, but through the glasses you can watch them for a long time. The red squirrels have practically gone ; the grey are everywhere. But because of the grey you will sometimes see, in the country, a pure white one, snowy and startling as it flashes upward in the black summer trees.

If we don't hunt him, they say, he will soon be extinct. And supposing he was? How many people, from one year's end to another, ever see a fox? How many would miss him if he were gone? Odd that we should show at once such callousness and such tender regard. Hunting a fox, tearing him to shreds with trained dogs, digging him out of drains—excellent ways of preventing his extinction. Shooting a fox—practically the same thing as shooting a sea-gull, beating a dog, or eating peas with a knife. Social privilege, social snobbery, social stupidity, social bitterness —odd, but very English, that an animal can be responsible for them all.

And who ever sees an otter? The trappings of the fox-hunt are absurd enough; the paraphernalia of the otter-hunt is comic opera for grown men. Half the sport is dressing up. Do small boys throw stones at cats?—a great reflection on their upbringing. But at selected seasons of the year you can come across grown men throwing dogs at otters. A great reflection too on their upbringing? Perhaps—but to say so is the equivalent of saying that a game with bat and ball which takes three days (or even eight days) to play, and even then isn't decided, is a stupid thing. This is sour talk. But somewhere behind the English attitude to foxes and horses, birds and dogs, cats and this beautiful shy nocturnal creature, the otter, lies a key, if we would trouble to look for it, to the national character.

On November 4, 1767, Gilbert White wrote to Thomas Pennington, 'I have procured some of the mice mentioned in my former
letter, a young one and a female with young, both of which I
have preserved in brandy. From the colour, shape, size and
manner of nesting, I make no doubt that the species is nondescript.
. . . They breed as many as eight in a litter, in a little round nest
comprised of the blades of grass or wheat. One of these nests I
procured this autumn, most artificially plaited, and composed
of the blades of wheat, perfectly round, and about the size of a
cricket-ball, with the aperture so ingeniously closed, that there
was no discovery to what part it belonged. . . . This wonderful
" procreant cradle," an elegant instance of the effects of instinct,
was found in a wheat-field suspended in the head of a thistle.'
And so was published the first account of the harvest mouse.

Two pictures of horses : the yeoman and the gypsy, the domestic and the wild. On Dartmoor and Exmoor and in the New Forest the gathering and scampering against the heather and the trees ; the long-skirted tails, the fiery timidity. On thousands of farms the ploughing team, the steadiness, the nobility, the symbolic harness brasses. Between the two lies much that is most loved in England : the placid cultivation, the unexpected wild ; the solid respectability of tradition, the gypsyish hedgerow. In a country like ours, where almost all the beauty of landscape is man-made, the bits of wild survival are precious. But we begin to cling too to the bit of civilised survival. The tractor overtakes the shire-horse, and our generation begins to look at him with sentimental affection : symbol of an age that was not disrupted. Small wonder, thinking of its solidity, simplicity and strength, all symbolised so well by the team at plough, that we begin to doubt our own.

CALENDAR FOR 1943

	JANUARY	FEBRUARY	MARCH	APRIL
S	.. 3 10 17 24 31	.. 7 14 21 28 ..	.. 7 14 21 28 ..	.. 4 11 18 25 ..
M	.. 4 11 18 25 ..	1 8 15 22	1 8 15 22 29 ..	.. 5 12 19 **26** ..
Tu	.. 5 12 19 26 ..	2 9 16 23	2 9 16 23 30 ..	.. 6 13 20 27 ..
W	.. 6 13 20 27 ..	3 10 17 24	3 10 17 24 31 ..	.. 7 14 21 28 ..
Th	.. 7 14 21 28 ..	4 11 18 25	4 11 18 25	1 8 15 22 29 ..
F	1 8 15 22 29 ..	5 12 19 26	5 12 19 26	2 9 16 **23** 30 ..
S	2 9 16 23 30 ..	6 13 20 27	6 13 20 27	3 10 17 24 .. ..

	MAY	JUNE	JULY	AUGUST
S	.. 2 9 16 23 30	.. 6 13 20 27 ..	.. 4 11 18 25 ..	1 8 15 22 29 ..
M	.. 3 10 17 24 31	.. 7 **14** 21 28 ..	.. 5 12 19 26 ..	**2** 9 16 23 30 ..
Tu	.. 4 11 18 25 ..	1 8 15 22 29 ..	.. 6 13 20 27 ..	3 10 17 24 31 ..
W	.. 5 12 19 26 ..	2 9 16 23 30 ..	.. 7 14 21 28 ..	4 11 18 25 .. ..
Th	.. 6 13 20 27 ..	3 10 17 24	1 8 15 22 29 ..	5 12 19 26 .. ..
F	.. 7 14 21 28 ..	4 11 18 25	2 9 16 23 30 ..	6 13 20 27 .. ..
S	1 8 15 22 29 ..	5 12 19 26	3 10 17 24 31 ..	7 14 21 28 .. ..

	SEPTEMBER	OCTOBER	NOVEMBER	DECEMBER
S	.. 5 12 19 26 ..	3 10 17 24 31	.. 7 14 21 28 ..	.. 5 12 19 26 ..
M	.. 6 13 20 27 ..	4 11 18 25 ..	1 8 15 22 29 ..	.. 6 13 20 **27** ..
Tu	.. 7 14 21 28 ..	5 12 19 26 ..	2 9 16 23 30 ..	.. 7 14 21 28 ..
W	1 8 15 22 29 ..	6 13 20 27 ..	3 10 17 24	1 8 15 22 29 ..
Th	2 9 16 23 30 ..	7 14 21 28 ..	4 11 18 25	2 9 16 23 30 ..
F	3 10 17 24	1 8 15 22 29 ..	5 12 19 26	3 10 17 24 31 ..
S	4 11 18 25	2 9 16 23 30 ..	6 13 20 27	4 11 18 **25** .. ..

Bank Holidays are shown in bold type

Nearly 4000 years ago in Egypt there died a steward named Senbi, and figures of men and animals were placed in his tomb for his use in the after life. Among them was this blue faience hippopotamus, which, with the other creatures mentioned here, is now in the Metropolitan Museum of Art in New York.

EGYPTIAN, 1950 B.C.

Faience figures of apes are also found in the Egyptian tombs. This one is glazed the blue of a robin's egg.

EGYPTIAN, 663–525 B.C.

253

More than twenty centuries after the Egyptian tomb figures were made, E. M. Sandoz carved this hen. He chose a piece of grey marble flecked with white.

FRENCH,
XX CENTURY

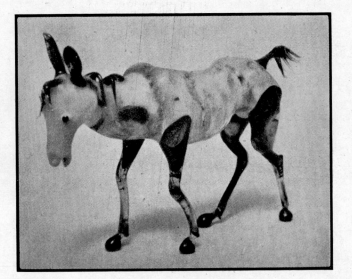

This Rosinante in glass was made by Marianna von Allesch.

AMERICAN,
XX CENTURY

A little bronze
horse marches
as if to music.

GREEK,
ABOUT 470
B.C.

Herbert Hasel-
tine has made a
collection of por-
traits of British
champions.
Here are Messa-
line and her foal.

AMERICAN,
XX CENTURY

In the 18th century the potters seemed to enjoy modelling animals, such as this deer, as a change from everlasting jugs and plates.

ENGLISH,
XVIII CENTURY

This Delft cow is very gay indeed. She has a bright blanket, a curled-up tail, and a frivolous eye.

DUTCH,
XVIII CENTURY

Probably the man who made this yellow cat intended to outline the eyes in brown. The glaze ran down and gave him a very woebegone cat indeed.

ENGLISH, STAFFORDSHIRE, XVIII CENTURY

The kittens are made of porcelain.

CHINESE, XVIII CENTURY

These three jerboa mice—jumping mice—are made of faience, glazed a soft white with brown markings.

EGYPTIAN, 2000—1788 B.C.

Jade has been the favourite medium of the Chinese for many centuries. This piece shades from a greenish white in the deer to a soft brown in leaves under their feet.

CHINESE,
XVIII CENTURY

Hollow tubes of glass and a Bunsen burner were used by Marianna von Allesch to create this toy. Dumbo might be his name.

AMERICAN,
XX CENTURY

Camels are often found among tomb figures in China. Those with saddle packs were intended as burden carriers for the soul on its journey after death.

CHINESE,
618–906

This peccary was carved by Georges Hilbert directly from a block of black granite.

FRENCH,
XX CENTURY

The ivory body
of the gazelle
was stained a
bright brown,
and the desert
flint under its
feet is dark.
The flowers are
the bluish green
of the sage
brush.

EGYPTIAN,
1375–1350 B.C.

Stoneware is the
sturdiest type of
pottery. Knud
Kyhn used it to
make this ape.

DANISH,
XX CENTURY

This polar bear was carved from white marble
by Francois Pompon.

FRENCH, XX CENTURY

The marble in this lion is mottled grey,
brown and yellow.

CHINESE, 618–906

This ibex formed the cheek-piece on a bridle of some nomad horseman of western Persia.

PERSIAN,
IX—VI
CENTURY

These gold quail were used as sword ornaments.

JAPANESE,
XIX CENTURY

The oxen were cast in bronze in the days of the Cæsars, probably as playthings.

ROMAN, I CENTURY B.C.—A.D. I CENTURY

This cock, by Pablo Gargallo, is made of wrought iron.

SPANISH,
XX CENTURY

The ivory elephant was a chess-piece.

MESOPOTAMIAN, OR INDIAN, VIII–X CENTURY

The rock crystal chosen for this rabbit is so clear that it seems to be made of ice.

CHINESE, 1736–1795

263

Illustrated by JACKS

THE CHIMPANZEE

The Chimpanzee [1] is found in Equatorial Africa and vaudeville. He is the brightest of the Anthropoid Apes because he is so classified by scientists with incomes over a thousand pounds. If the scientist places a banana in a box the Chimpanzee will go and get it and eat it. The Chimpanzee also likes hominy, lettuce, raspberries, weak tea and black beetles. Chimpanzees are highly excitable and partly web-footed. They are amusing but terribly shallow. They can be very trying. The love life of Chimpanzees is about what you might expect. When a Chimpanzee looks at another Chimp he does not see what we see. They frequently have twins. Chimpanzee sweethearts say very little. They can say 'Yes' and 'No' and 'Thank you very much.' [2] They can count up to five. They are faithful within reason. In the Chimpanzee the hallux is opposable and the pollex is not. In Man it is just the other way round, so it all comes out even. The Chimpanzee smokes, rides a bicycle and wears pants. His chief ambition is an engagement at the Palladium. The Chimpanzee has one-third enough brain, and that's something. Or is it ?

[1] Aristotle did not mention Chimps, but they got along somehow.
[2] What they really say is *gak gak*, *ngak ngak* and *wha wha*. Chimpanzees find these words sufficient for all practical purposes.

THE GORILLA

After a Chimp the Gorilla is a great relief. He is fierce and brutal and is not a mimic. He weighs four hundred and fifty pounds and is named Bobby. Young Gorillas are friendly, but they soon learn. When a banana is placed in a trick box within easy reach the Gorilla will bite the professor's cousin. Guess what that proves. The Gorilla is becoming extinct, but there are plenty of professors. In affairs of the heart the male Gorilla is slow but sure. He appears to be stolid and indifferent, but that may be part of his system.[1] Believe it or not, he is shy. Married females and their children sleep in trees and the male sleeps on the ground. The meaning of this is unknown. The Gorilla could do with more brains. Gorillas like sugar-cane, hay, watermelons, ragout of chicken, raw ham, dandelions and lollypops. They are subject to inflammation of the gums. Female Gorillas are likely to bump into passing objects and have trouble with revolving doors. I am in favour of Gorillas. They live in Africa.

The Gorilla is said to have hidden depths, but if they are so hidden, what good are they? He has small ears, generally a bad sign.

THE ORANG-UTAN

Orang-utans teach us that looks are not everything but darned near it.[1] They look awful. Some Orang-utans have huge cheek-pads and conspicuous laryngeal sacs. Others have worse. The hallux is undeveloped. The female is not so ugly, but ugly enough. Both sexes brood a lot. Their prolonged spells of meditation appear to have no tangible results. Orangs often sleep on one arm and wake up with a cramp. They snore. Young Orangs who are permitted to develop their individualities turn out horribly. Young Orangs who are kicked and beaten into line also turn out horribly. The psychology of the Orang-utan has been thoroughly described by scientists from their observation of the Sea-urchin. Other facts have been gathered from the natives of Borneo and Sumatra who may have been talking about something else at the time. There is considerable doubt whether the Orang-utan is as dumb as he seems or dumber. He likes stewed apples, toast, cocoa and soap. Orang-utans have solved the problem of work. They do not work. They never worry. And yet they have wrinkles. So what's the use?

[1] About 93 per cent.

THE GIBBON

Those thin long-waisted types with no head to speak of are generally Gibbons. Gibbons are our loudest Apes. Their peculiar cry is often described as *hoo hoo hoo hoo* and just as often as *whopp whopp whopp whopp*. Gibbons assemble in crowds and *hoo* or *whopp* until exhausted or shot. The natives of Cochin China, the Malay Archipelago and the Island of Hainan often have *hoo* or *whopp* madness. A noiseless Gibbon would be a godsend. There is an old saying that the Gibbon is at his best in the American Museum of Natural History.[1] The female Wau-wau or Silvery Gibbon of Java is rather pretty for a Wau-wau. The Hoolock of Upper Assam cannot swim. Gibbons are noted for the number and variety of things they cannot do. It is believed that the Gibbon could be taught to swat flies. Gibbons live in the tree-tops. They swing from branch to branch by their arms with amazing speed. They are not going to fires. They are going nowhere in particular. Experiments with the Gibbon prove many interesting things about the Long-nosed Bandicoot. Gibbon authorities do not know whether the Gibbon is interested in sex. But you know and I know. There are no Apes in this country, thank goodness.[2]

[1] Cf. *Decline and Fall of the Gibbon.*

[2] Embalmed Gibbons are sometimes sold to country bumpkins as embalmed Pigmies. Why our rural population should prefer embalmed Pigmies to embalmed Gibbons offers an interesting problem in psychology.

THE BABOON

The Baboon is entirely uncalled for. Some people like Baboons, but something is wrong with such people. Baboons lose their tempers. There are more Baboons than you might think. The Baboon is not an Anthropoid Ape. He has a tail, though not a good one, and so he is a Lower Ape. In fact he is more of a Monkey. The Arabian Baboon, as the name implies, is found in Abyssinia. Baboons have highly coloured ischial callosities. Scientists tell us that all animals who sit down a great deal have ischial callosities. That is a lie. The Mandrill is the worst, especially when going South. Baboons bark. It seems as though there would be no female Baboons, but there are. The family life of the Baboon is known as hell on earth. The males grow meaner and stingier and the females fade at an early age. The children scream, stamp, roll on the ground and will not eat their Centipedes. Their parents are proud of them.[1] The Sacred Baboon of the Egyptians was identified with Thoth, the god of literary criticism.[2] He spent his time making Thothlike motions at the Sacred Ibis, another form of literary criticism.[2] He is not yet extinct. Never call any one a Baboon unless you are sure of your facts. Baboons have flat feet.

[1] Young Baboons ride pick-a-back.
[2] He is frequently pictured restoring the Udjat or Eye to Aah, the Moon God. Enormous numbers of Udjats have been found in Ancient Egyptian tombs. 'The twin Udjats represent the Eye of the Sun and the Eye of the Moon.'—Sir E. A. Wallis Budge.

The Howling Monkey is confined to South America, but seems to escape. The back of his head is straight up and down. His howl is caused by a large hyoid bone at the top of the trachea. It can be cured by a simple operation on the neck with an axe. The male Howler is always followed by seven or eight female Howlers with young Howlers, but this may be a coincidence. Howlers have long prehensile tails with which they hang from the trees, talk Monkey talk and pick up Brazil nuts. There are several species of Howlers. The Fat Howler is as trying as any. The Howling Monkey and the Spider Monkey are neighbours. The infant Howling Monkey occasionally bears a striking resemblance to a Spider Monkey. Ask me some time why that is.[1] The Capuchin or Organ Grinder Monkey is regarded as very intelligent. He scrambles after pennies, scratches himself, and has morals. He can stand on his hind legs, but the tail is a dead give-away.[2] Monkeys have loads of fun. They breed in captivity and know many other tricks. They are fond of Bats, marshmallows, Goldfish and ink. Old World Monkeys cannot hang by their tails. They might as well not be Monkeys.[3]

[1] Spider Monkeys look nothing like Spiders.

[2] The Tee-tee or Squirrel Monkey inhabits Brazil and the Reading Room of the British Museum.

[3] There is a general feeling among Old World Monkeys that they are the best Monkeys, but there is no scientific basis for this. If you are an Old World Monkey you are classed as Catarrhine or narrow-nosed. If not, you are Platyrrhine or broad-nosed. That's about the gist of it.

THE LEMUR

The Lemur is one worse than the Monkey. He is often mistaken for a Squirrel, a Rabbit, an Agouti or anything but a Lemur. He has been described as a state of mind or ectoplasm. The Lemur is a Primate because people say so. The Lemur sleeps all day long and nobody tells him that he is a tramp. When disturbed he sort of squeaks. Most Lemurs live in Madagascar, but they are never quite warm enough. The Ring-tailed Lemur or Madagascar Cat[1] is caught by sailors who have enough Parrots already. The Gentle Lemur is devoted to his human keeper and often bites him severely. The Aye-aye has large movable ears caused by listening for Grubs. The Potto is rather peevish. The Spectral Tarsier of the West Indies is uncanny. He has huge bug-eyes, elongated ankles and knobby toes. He is sometimes confused with Delirium Tremens. Lemurs comb their hair with their lower front teeth. They mature almost instantaneously. In a way we came from Lemurs because they are also descended from an extinct Tree Shrew, something like a large Rat. From the Tree Shrew to the Dogfish is but a step, which practically brings us to the Amoeba. So perhaps the Lemur is to blame for it all.[2]

---

[1] *Lemur catta.*
[2] Aristotle would not have known a Lemur if it came up and bit him. He had enough to keep track of, without Lemurs.

═COMPETITION═

This competition is concerned, in a primitive and personal sense, with post-war planning. Its seven photographs all relate to pleasures we shall one day resume—No. 1, for example, is seeing London ablaze with lights, Nos. 2 and 3 are matters of food. Competitors are asked, bearing in mind the theme of 'what I shall do when peace comes,' to single out for study any three of the photographs and write down what they regard as the appropriate comments or captions for them. Length may be anything from one to fifty words in each case ; or not more than fourteen lines of verse. The number of the photograph should be prefixed to the comment.

Four prizes of War Savings Certificates will be awarded, two for entries received up to January 31, 1943, two for those received after that but not later than June 30, 1943, which is the closing date. Address entries to COMPETITION, THE SATURDAY BOOK, 47, Princes Gate, S.W.7. The Editor's decision is final.

Photographs by DOUGLAS GLASS

2

3

4

5

6

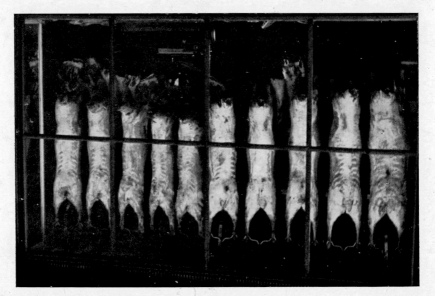

7